Association for the Welfare
of Children in Hospital

June 1975.   LIBRARY NO. 20(a)

Play in Hospital

Play in Hospital

Edited by

Susan Harvey and
Ann Hales-Tooke, M.A.

Advisers

Eva Noble and
David Morris, M.R.C.S., F.R.C.P., D.C.H.

Faber and Faber
3 Queen Square
London

Published 1972 by
Faber and Faber Limited
3 Queen Square, London WC1
Printed in Great Britain at The Pitman Press, Bath

ISBN 0 571 09827 4

CONTENTS

5

List of Illustrations

List of figures

List of Plates

9

Preface

In 1966 the UK National Committee of the World Organization for Early Childhood Education (OMEP)* sponsored a working party to consider the value of play for children in hospital. As a result the report *Play in Hospital* was produced by people actively concerned with the well-being of children in hospital. This study included the provision of play for children of all ages from infancy to adolescence who were treated in the children's wards. It was unanimously agreed that if children in hospital were to have a new deal, unrestricted visiting and generous arrangements for play must be organized. Play schemes have since been introduced into many hospitals and we hope the experience which has been gained and which is recorded in this book will be useful for those who promote play or who specialize in providing play for sick and handicapped children in any setting.

Susan Harvey, 1971

---

* Organisation Mondiale pour l'Education Préscolaire.

Acknowledgements

We would like to express our warm appreciation and thanks to those who have helped us.

Dr. Mary D. Sheridan, M.A., M.D., D.C.H., for her advice on Chapter 1.

Mrs. Nora Williams, Lecturer in Child Development, Southwark College for Further Education, for observations and diagrams for Chapter 1.

Miss Phyllis Asquith, S.R.N., Matron, Pensby Wing, Clatterbridge Hospital, Cheshire, and

Dr. Edna Oakeshott, Lecturer, University of London Institute of Education for their contributions and advice on Chapter 3.

Lady Allen of Hurtwood, Founder Member of OMEP.

Miss J. Cass, representing the Nursery School Association of Great Britain and Northern Ireland and former Lecturer at the University of London Institute of Education, and

Miss Isobel Menzies, Consultant psycho-analyst and social psychologist, for their contributions and advice on the OMEP report, *Play in Hospital* (1966).

Mrs. G. Marston, SCF hospital playleader, and
Miss J. Young, SCF hospital supervisor, for their
advice and support.

All SCF hospital playleaders whose work and
reports have been extensively used throughout
this book.

The Save The Children Fund, which has promoted
and sponsored play schemes for children in
many hospitals.
Camilla Jessel for photographs provided by SCF
and hospitals which gave us their permission
(for details of plates see p. 9).
Audrey Besterman for the line drawings.

The following hospitals kindly gave permission for
us to use their photographs

Charing Cross Hospital (Fulham) for Plates 4, 6,
8, 9 and 12
The London Hospital   for Plates 2, 3 and 10
Mile End Hospital   for Plate 11
St Charles' Hospital   for Plates 5 and 7

Introduction

by Dr. David Morris, F.R.C.P., D.C.H.

The welfare of children in hospital is the concern of parents, doctors, nurses and administrators. Total medical care entails not only the highest possible standard of diagnosis and treatment but also designing the whole experience in such a way that a child will be helped to withstand the inevitable effects of his illness, his separation from home and family and his entry into a new, strange, and different world. A young child who is ill and has to be treated in hospital has a lot to contend with, which may be upsetting and have far-reaching effects. He has to adjust to a bewildering array of different sounds, smells and sights, to a different bed in a different place, and with a whole variety of people in different uniforms who come and go with little, if any, continuity or close care by one person for any period of time. Strange, often frightening and painful things are done to him, all of which he has to deal with as best he can at the same time as being ill.

Because of this, efforts have been made to avoid the admission of children into hospital whenever possible: Dr. Rex Laurie has shown that many operations can be carried out on a day basis. To help children while they are in hospital unrestricted visiting has become more widespread and parents are encouraged to visit as much as possible. There are facilities in some hospitals for mothers to stay with their children.

A further development for the well-being of children in hospital has been the provision for play by playleaders, employed for the purpose and using suitable play materials and equipment. This is one way in which a child's life in

15

hospital is made less unnatural, and the enjoyment it brings counteracts in no small measure the unavoidable and inevitable discomfort, disease, pain and misery a child may have to go through. The doctors and nurses may well rely on the playleader to be a source of comfort when unpleasant procedures have to be carried out, to console the child afterwards and help him towards recovery. It is hoped that this service will become an established part of the care of children in hospital, and professionally recognized as the other auxiliary services.

While the main purpose of providing hospital care for children is to diagnose, treat and restore ill children to health, we have in the last twenty-five years become sensitively aware of what being in hospital can mean to a child, and the harmful emotional effects this can have. The continuity of family ties and close contact with parents is important for young children. The provision of play by playleaders not only makes their time in hospital more enjoyable, but meaningful by the opportunity it provides for self-expression and a possible influence for their recovery. It is hoped that the basic principles entailed in play with children in hospital will eventually be incorporated into paediatric nursing.

Illness is never without interference and effect on our lives. If it is a minor complaint of short duration it may leave little, if any, after-effect, and there will be a quick restoration to health. The effect of more serious illness will be influenced by the child's age and what toll it takes of him. If he has to be admitted to hospital, then he has in addition to the effect of the illness to cope with all that being in hospital entails. How much pain and immobility he sustains, the discomfort of the procedures he undergoes are all factors which will affect him.

Working with children necessitates adaptation by adults to children's needs. Children are not miniature adults, but individuals with their own particular endowment, who come from families of many kinds. The way they are spoken to in hospital and the manner in which they are handled may be a new experience. Sometimes they may be treated with respect and recognition of their needs, or they may be disregarded or ignored. The child who comes into hospital knowing something about it or having previously played at it will often be in a better frame of mind than the child who has been threatened by admission to hospital as a punishment for being naughty (which still occurs far too often). Young children are dominated by their feelings but gradually the development of intellect influences them to behave more rationally. They react in an 'all or none' way to pleasant and unpleasant experiences and are comforted by feeding when hungry and respond to the warmth and closeness of a loving adult. They rapidly develop skills of identification of persons and sources of pleasure and these skills they bring with them into hospital. Under the age of two and a half years a child's reaction to his environment tends to be total. He can only be reasoned with up to a point and it does not take a lot to upset him and stop him from co-operating.

Schaffer[1] has shown that babies under seven months of age do not appear to be unduly upset by being in hospital. They may be quieter or cry more than they do at home but they are as responsive to the nurses as to their mothers, without becoming upset when they leave. When they return home they tend to be quiet and subdued and appear preoccupied with their environment, looking and staring at things a lot of the time. It is difficult to distract them, and mothers find it hard to re-establish their previous contact: Schaffer calls this the 'global syndrome' and ascribes it to the perceptual monotony of their time in hospital. The playleader, by providing stimulation, can

---

[1] Schaffer, H. R. and Callendar, W. M.: 'Psychological Effects of Hospitalization in Infancy', *Journal of Paediatrics*, 1959, **24**, p. 528.

reduce the monotony these babies experience. Our professional task is to understand and do all we can to support mothers during this experience. We should welcome them into hospital, encourage them to look after their own babies, bolster up their confidence and help them overcome their trepidation.

Infants over seven months of age show their response to hospital: they cry a lot and tend to be withdrawn, react anxiously to anybody who approaches them and when they see their mothers they often become inconsolable, clinging to them while they are there and distraught when they leave. This may change after a week or so when they may become more responsive to strangers. On returning home they may cling to their mothers all the time and appear fearful of their departure.

How old are children when they can manage this experience without too much upset? Prugh and his colleagues[1] in Boston have shown that up to four years of age children continue to react in this way even when the conditions, attitudes, and practices of the professionals in hospital are ideal. It docs seem as though the presence of mothers minimizes the degree of disturbance experienced in hospital, and the after-effects. Mothers, by their presence, seem to enable the children to deal with their anxieties. This research team showed that children in this age group with previous traumatic experience reacted with great distress, as did children who had unusual relationships with their parents. Hospital staff often expect children who come from unhappy homes to cope better with being in hospital: but the fortunate child who has a warm loving mother image in his mind is in a stronger position to deal with the ordeal of being ill and away from home.

---

[1] Prugh, D. G., Staub, E. M., Sands, H. H., Kirschbaum, R. M., and Lenihan, E. A.: 'A Study of the Emotional Reactions of Children and Families to Hospitalization and Illness,' *American Journal of Orthopsychiatry*, 1953, **23**, p. 70.

Doctors and nurses who work with children in hospital have in one sense an unenviable task. They have to be responsible for children who may be seriously ill, in severe pain, in the terminal stages of disease, or suffering from disfiguring or crippling illness. For much of the time they have the burden of children's unhappiness and the added distress caused by the things they do to them. No one can deny this is a tough assignment and often a distressing experience which can make them feel anxious and guilty, and which may interfere with their work and efficiency. In order to deal with these situations they become clinically detached, whilst at the same time trying hard not to lose their sympathy and kind feelings for the individual child; a difficult and challenging balance. It is more common for them to develop a defence against their subjective feelings by unknowingly denying the serious emotional events children are experiencing. Fortunately some children have the resilience to deal satisfactorily with their illness and their experience in hospital.

Doctors are involved with the child and his family in a different way from nurses—their role is well defined: essentially that of diagnosis and treatment for the quickest cure. The emphasis on diagnosis and treatment has often been at the expense of the patient as a person. Paediatricians have contributed towards a change in this attitude by their interest in the individual child and his illness, rather than in the illness alone. The previous state of affairs was perhaps more convenient for doctors.

Priorities and exigencies are dominant factors in hospital and affect everyone who is involved. The demands for immediate and rapid action with skilled technical efficiency may have to be at the expense of a more leisurely and considerate attitude towards the patient. In contrast to adults it may not be possible to have the patient's co-operation, for he may be too young to understand what is happening to him. Whenever possible some simple explanation should be attempted and for those who are too young to comprehend we should appreciate their need for cuddling and physical comfort.

Auxiliary nurses, laboratory technicians, ward maids, orderlies and porters are all part of a child's hospital experience. Sometimes, because their roles are not so well defined as the doctors' and nurses', they can form a significant relationship with a particular child. Children meet many people fleetingly—nurses with their off-duty times and doctors whom they may not see regularly. The playleader also has her hours of work, sometimes working in the morning, sometimes all day, rarely during the early evening or at weekends. Laboratory technicians are seldom trained to establish a relationship with a child before sticking a needle into him. Ward orderlies and porters have to transport children to different departments and may be solely responsible for the child, but how often do they talk to him or explain where they are going and what it will be like? If we are to be concerned with the welfare of children in hospital, we have to pay attention to these important details.

Illness means dependency. Going to bed and being looked after when we are adults is an experience we often relish. Anna Freud[1] has shown that children differ from adults in this respect; they are not so ready to give up what they have recently learned and all that was entailed in achieving their newly acquired independence. This threatened loss makes them difficult, miserable and unhappy. Some children slip back into a previous dependent stage of infancy, others fight it by being excessively active, resistant to immobilization, aggressive, restless and irritable. Here again the playleader can reassure them by providing them with occupations they can successfully

---

[1] Freud, A.: 'The Role of Bodily Illness in the Mental Life of Children,' *Psycho-Analytic Study of the Child*, 1952, **8**, p. 69.

manage by themselves. There is the added disappointment which comes from the realization that it takes time before they can do what they did before: they cannot accept that they are not completely better the moment they come out of plaster. It is probably not until they are well past four years old that they can begin to gain anything profitable from such an experience.

In an attempt to minimize these harmful effects we have tried to find ways of doing this such as by unrestricted visiting, the facility for mothers and children to be in hospital together, the preparation of children for coming into hospital by using toys and stories, the provision of play facilities and a playleader and above all a sympathetic and understanding attitude.

Play in Hospital from o to 5 years

THE IMPORTANCE OF PLAY

We are so used to seeing children at play that it is easy to overlook its importance. Play is not just a way of passing the time and keeping the young from interfering with the serious business of adults. It is a vital part of child development.

Deprived of play, the child is a prisoner, shut off from all that makes life real and meaningful. Play is not merely a means of learning the skills of daily living. The impulse to create and achieve, working through play, allows the child to grow in body and mind. There is as great a drive in play to persevere to a real and desired end, to overcome difficulties and to concentrate on the matter in hand, as there is in work. In play, however, there is no compulsion, except perhaps, in the play behaviour of the very neurotic or seriously disturbed child. Play can be indulged in or laid aside at will. It is its own final justification; and the intense pleasure and delight that children derive from it is enough in itself to convince us of its value.

The world is not an easy place in which to live and grow up. Play is one of the ways in which a child may develop a capacity to deal with the stresses and strains of life as they press upon him. It acts, too, as a safety valve, allowing him to re-live, and often come to terms with fears and anxieties which become overwhelming. Life contains many frustrations but the ability to overcome them provides a positive sense of achievement. If, however, frustrations are overwhelming, despair and lack of confidence may well be the result.

Children are denied many things they want; they are expected to conform to a standard of behaviour which they do not yet understand; and they cannot easily put their difficulties and perplexities into words. In vigorous, lively and creative or destructive play, with access to the right kind of materials, children are able to find satisfying and legitimate outlets for their tensions and conflicts.

In dramatic games of all kinds, dressing-up, playing mothers and fathers, cops and robbers, they pretend to be the strong and powerful adults they both envy and admire so much. Children escape into a world of fantasy where hopes and fears come true. This world can set the seal, as it were, on a re-lived experience or provide a practice ground for later tasks. To work through a genuine fear, loss or jealousy in an imaginative setting can often make these feelings more tolerable in real life.

Susan Isaacs points out that, 'Imaginative play builds a bridge by which a child can pass from the symbolic value of things to active inquiry into their real construction and way of working'.

The world around is full of objects children want to touch and handle, examine and experiment with. Children are endowed with boundless curiosity and a passionate desire to find out all they can about the environment in which they live. In learning skills, how to dress a doll, wield a hammer or ride a tricycle, they are gaining not only knowledge but confidence and independence. In physical activity too, in running, jumping, climbing, children discover how to use their bodies with poise and agility. Their abundant energy and vitality suggest all sorts of exciting and challenging outlets.

Children make their first tentative social relationships outside the home where their play brings them into contact with other children. They gradually begin to value friendship and to be aware of each other's needs and wishes; with difficulty they learn to share their toys and

24

to co-operate happily together. The development of language helps to stabilize these contacts both with other children and with adults.

Every child needs to be treated as an individual. He develops in his own way—physically, intellectually, emotionally—and at his own pace. Each child varies in the age at which he goes through the broad stages of development, such as walking, reading and the ability to tolerate brief separation from mother.

Partly because they do not have sufficient command of language children express their feelings through play, assimilating experience, sorting out fact from fiction, and rehearsing what they think may happen to them in the future. In a way it is a concrete form of talking to themselves. Over and over again they play out experiences and learn to manage situations over which they have no control. Sometimes their reasons are obvious.

For example, when Timmy aged 4 and Anna aged 5 were disappointed because they could not go out for a walk with their parents, Timmy went to the toy shelf and threw all his Dinky Toy cars on the floor and kicked them. Anna retreated to a corner and picked up a rag doll and sucked its leg and refused to move. After a short time they both felt better and returned to active play.

Often there appears to be a necessity to play out a situation when its logical cause is by no means clear.

For example, Jenny aged 7 watched a wedding from the window and for several weeks after she wore a long white lace skirt all day long even if she was climbing trees or digging in the sand. Although her parents did not know why she did this they felt it was important for her to act in this way.

Children will use all the material they can find for their play so that the more primitive and unstructured it is, the more adaptable it will be for their purposes. Play is, among other things, a self-initiated and a self-healing activity and each child will know what he wants at any given moment. Charley aged 2 banging two bricks together may be enjoying the use of his limbs, the noise he is making, or giving vent to aggression. He may be doing all these things at once. While playing this game he is certainly learning something about the co-ordination of eye and limbs and gaining concepts of time and space. Just as there are no real frontiers between different kinds of play there are no real frontiers between playthings. At any moment a stick may become a weapon, a tool, a doll or a companion. In the early stages of life, education, play and work are indivisible facets of living. Effort, concentration and persistence are apparent all along the line.

The deeply unhappy child cannot play. The child who is able to play may be seen to be working through his tensions and anxieties to achieve a state of absorption leading to satisfaction and happiness. Happiness is a quality which defies scientific measurement but when felt undoubtedly contributes to health and recovery.

The child who cannot play freely with objects of his own choice throughout the formative years may develop a limited view of reality and of his own capabilities.

SPECIAL VALUE OF PLAY FOR THE CHILD IN HOSPITAL

The full value of play to children in hospital is only realized when a wide range of simple natural play materials and activities are provided and each child, within the limits which his illness, treatment or handicap impose, is free to choose what he will play with.

This kind of play when not being undertaken by parents or friends is most beneficial when supervised by experienced and highly qualified people such as nursery and primary school teachers or senior nursery nurses. If children are deeply disturbed the help of a child psycho-therapist is necessary.

What then does the child in hospital specially need from his play? He is away from home in a strange and sometimes frightening environment, surrounded by people he does not know and experiencing events he cannot predict, control or understand. His need to play out his anxieties and problems is urgent and demanding. Young children have very strong feelings of love and hate to-wards those they care most about and on whom they are most dependent. The hostile feelings a child may have, both towards his parents who have seemingly deserted him and towards the hospital staff who may cause him to suffer pain as well as alleviate it, must have an outlet.

Some children will want to remember things from home in their play so that their warm and loving feelings towards their parents and their trust in the world as a whole are supported and strengthened.

A child may develop some skill with paint or paper, complete a puzzle over and over again, dress a doll and in so doing reassure himself that he can still use his body and limbs successfully. This in itself can give him immense relief. By occupying himself in creative activities he is, in a sense, repairing those parts of himself which he feels have been broken or damaged.

To lie in bed, perhaps with nothing to do, in unfamiliar surroundings, watching treatment being given to other children, hearing sounds of crying from behind screens, can be most alarming. Then, perhaps with little warning or explanation, painful things from which there is no escape are done to the child. The adult may try to explain what is involved in the treatment he must undergo, the anaesthetic he must take, the discomfort he may suffer; but how much can he really understand when he feels lost and forsaken and has no previous experience on which to draw?

One of the important ways in which to help him to manage some of these painful events is to provide the right kind of play, so that he can gradually externalize his fears, slowly accept them and adapt them to suit his private personal requirements. Contacts with other boys and girls in the ward can be stimulated. Talk and laughter, painful and unusual procedures can all be shared. Children learn much from each other even when they cannot play actively together.

While some children are less vulnerable, others will be so shocked by what has happened that they appear 'frozen' and withdrawn, with little or no response to any of the activities offered or to the person who offers them. It will take time and great understanding to help these children to return to their human contacts and their play. Others may be ready and eager to use anything they are given. All of them not only need to 'play out' their feelings while they are in hospital; they also need to 'play out' their feelings when they return home.

Wherever a young child is, at home or in hospital, he will want the constant support of a warm and loving adult. The playleader will always supplement but never supplant the parents' role. As well as organizing the play activities in hospital she can often suggest to an anxious parent the kind of occupation which would be acceptable at a given moment or produce a suitable book for mother or father to read to the patient. In the absence of parents, she will try temporarily to act in their place.

It must be remembered at all times when dealing with sick children that they regress from their actual age and normal stage of development. For instance, the five-year-old who is ill will probably be quite happy to play with farm and zoo animals usually played with by normal, healthy three- and four-year-olds. Left to himself a sick child will often choose the toys and games he played with at an earlier age. Often he cannot play with as much concentration and persistence as when he was well. As he recovers, his ability to concentrate returns. While sick he may tire easily. All playthings given to sick children should be easy to manage and to manipulate. Anything too 'fiddly' will quickly frustrate the sick child.

Research studies show that children under the age of three to four years suffer predominantly from anxiety at being separated from their mothers. With their limited sense of reality they grieve over the loss of parents and home surroundings. Children in this category need the active approach of one playleader who will make herself available to these 'lost' children. It may take some time for the relationship to build up and for the children to become absorbed once more in active play.

Older children with a better understanding of reality are more consciously disturbed by fears of the treatment procedures and are pre-occupied by fantasies of severe bodily damage and even total destruction. These children need the playleader to discuss their problems with them. At the same time they find companions of their own age and while they give mutual support to each other they engage in active play needing the playleader only for guidance and supervision.

THE FIRST STAGE OF PLAY
(Ego-centric; sensory-motor)
Children from about 1 month to 12 months

In her book *The Activity of Children*, P. M. Pickard writes '. . . Research workers are very careful about ages and stages of development. Children differ in many ways. Some have greater and some lesser gifts; some are advanced in one thing and not in another. . . . Each child is unique. Adults could save themselves much worry if they understood this'.[1]

---

[1] *The Activity of Children*. P. M. Pickard. Longmans, 1965.

Ages and stages are used in this book as an approximate guide to any particular child's development and needs. Some perfectly normal children take much longer than others to reach a developmental stage. For example, some normal babies walk at 9 months, others at 18 months or even later.

The beginning of learning

The baby begins to discover his environment and his capabilities by touch, taste, sight, hearing, smell and movement. He uses his mouth as a way of learning. He sucks and then by chance discovers he can suck his fists. This provides the sensation of sucking and being sucked. Later a variety of objects will find their way to his mouth. These simple things (spoons, blankets, rattles, rings, etc.) must be safe and washable. Conventional toys are scarcely necessary. He will enjoy colours, textures and playthings which can be grasped, cuddled or which make a noise. He will be active and learning all the time he is awake and needs maximum opportunity for exploring. Even at this early age the baby is a going concern and interacts with his mother. He begins to watch her nearby face when she feeds or talks to him, and he utters little throaty noises when content.[1]

Development in Relation to Play[2]
Age about One Month

Development in relation to play	**Suggestions for play provision in hospital**
Sleeps most of the time when not being fed or handled.	Preferably only one play-leader to co-operate with mother and nurses in the

[1] 'The Developmental Progress of Infants and Young Children,' Mary D. Sheridan, M.A., M.D., D.C.H. *Reports on Public Health and Medical Subjects.* No. 102, H.M.S.O. 1967.

[2] *Ibid.*

Begins to watch mother's face as she feeds him.
Startled by sudden loud noises.
Stops whimpering to sound of a soothing human voice.
May stop crying when picked up.

care of each baby. The baby needs close physical contact. Should be carried around in arms if condition permits it. Babies need to be talked to although they may not yet be able to show a response.

Nurse on lap.
They get this kind of handling at home so they need it even more in hospital.

Age about Three Months

Development in relation to play

Suggestions for play provision in hospital

Visually alert. Moves head to look around, follows adults' movements near cot. Kicks vigorously, clasps and unclasps hands. Grasps toys placed in his hands.
Still distressed by loud noises.
Responds to mother's voice.
Reacts with smiles and excited movements to familiar situations such as feeds, baths, etc.
Enjoys friendly handling.

As well as being carried around and played with on the lap, the baby should be taken from his cot for some time each day to play freely on a rug on the floor.
He should be encouraged to move his limbs, kick, stretch, roll and to lie on his back and stomach.
Talking and singing to him are important.

A variety of toys can be attached to strings and

rods across the cot, such as rattles, bobbins, wooden spoons, soft toys, etc.

Enjoys being propped up by firm cushions or being placed in a baby seat so that he can watch what is going on round him.

Must be watched carefully for signs of tiredness.

Age about Six Months

Development in relation to play

Moves head and eyes in every direction.
When hands are grasped pulls himself up.
Kicks strongly.
When held in standing position with feet touching on hard surface bears weight on feet and bounces up and down.

Laughs, chuckles and uses single syllable sounds.
Screams when annoyed.
Reaches and grasps small toys.
Can hold objects.
Interested in own hands and feet.

Suggestions for play provision in hospital

Toys hanging across cot arranged so that when baby relinquishes them he can find them again. (See Fig. 4, p. 86.)
It is important to ensure that suspended toys are at the correct distance and height for each child.

There should be frequent opportunities for adult and child to play together, including the adult grasping the child's hand and holding him in a position to encourage him to get the feel of his feet.

Shakes rattles to make a noise.
Shows displeasure when toys are removed.
Shows some shyness to strangers.
Recognizes mother's voice.
Takes everything to mouth.

Rattles, improvised and ready-made, give pleasure, as well as toys with squeakers or with bells (check for safety).
Wooden spoons, rings, etc., to hold and bite on.

Age about Nine Months

Development in relation to play

Suggestions for play provision in hospital

Sits alone for 10 to 15 minutes on floor, stretches out for dangling toy or picks up one near him.
Moves by rolling and attempts to crawl.
Can stand holding on to a support but cannot lower himself.

If held in correct position steps out as if to walk.
Examines objects with great interest. Grasps and holds out toy but cannot give it up.

Begins to search for lost toys.
Plays 'peep-bo'.

At this stage every effort must be made to give the child opportunities to crawl around and explore his surroundings.
He should spend some time daily on a rug on the floor, as well as being carried as far afield as possible.
A playpen can be used.
Large balls and rolling pins will encourage movement.
He can play with bricks, boxes and other sturdy toys on the floor, including such things as empty talcum powder tins and cotton reels, etc.

Vocalizes as a means of communication, shouts to attract attention, babbles and tries to imitate adults' playful sounds.

Distinguishes strangers from familiar people—some shyness.

If a child at this stage is in plaster or otherwise immobilized it is important to give him opportunities to unload his frustration—wooden spoons and hammers to bang about with, drums, bells, etc. It may be possible to carry him or wheel him in pram or trolley so that he sees something of the outside world beyond his cot and ward. He enjoys being taken to look out of the window. Rattles and drums, rhythmic games and songs and above all conversation are an essential part of his daily programme.

An 'odds and ends' box or basket

This is an excellent way of providing playthings for babies in the first and second stages of play. It can contain a whole variety of oddments which are more satisfying than the usual toys, such as: lids, tins (smoothly finished), cardboard boxes, round and square pegs, wooden spoons, spatulas, rubber dog bones, safely-sealed tins containing such things as dried peas, beans, grain, bells to rattle. Large pebbles, sponges, wooden blocks, tins covered in fabric, Fablon, towelling and corduroy are satisfying to handle; also wooden hammers, keys on a ring, cowbell and bobbins. By 12 months, babies are fascinated by dropping balls into a tin or box with a hole in. It is lost from sight but they know it is there and search to re-discover it.

This game links with playing 'peep-bo'. Somewhere between 9 and 12 months the baby, sitting up in pram or cot, begins to throw his toys away—at the same time demanding that they should be picked up and returned to him. This is a persistent and universal game where the willingness of the adult is stretched to the limit! It is just as if the baby is asking the question, 'Do things which are lost return again?' or, 'Does mother re-appear when she goes out of sight?' Implicit in this is the gradual discovery of 'me, you and it'.

It seems that each child gradually becomes aware that when mother goes away she is likely to return again, and that when he goes away he has the power to bring his mother back again when he emerges from his hiding place. When the child can tolerate longer separations this game develops into 'hide and seek', but in the beginning the only time the baby knows is the present. This game of 'peep-bo' and throwing away toys has a special importance in hospital where separation is involved and it is wise for nurse and playleader to be patient enough to play it as often as the child demands it.

Examples of Play with Children in Hospital

Sandra (5 months)

She was admitted for failure to thrive. The consultant asked for extra care to be given to her. The nurses and playleader co-operated to give her constant attention. For three weeks she spent most of the mornings in the arms or on the lap of the playleader. Mother came every afternoon from a long distance. The nurses gave her all the time they could. In two weeks Sandra was smiling, grasping and reaching for toys and putting on weight. In the third week she was kicking contentedly on a rug for twenty minutes at a time.

Neville (7 months)

He was a neglected child from a large family admitted with a skin condition and confined to a cubicle. He was rarely visited. The ward sister asked the playleader to give him a great deal of attention. At first he took no notice of people and never smiled. He lay still and passive. The playleader spent time with him at frequent intervals throughout each day. After six days he smiled at the sound of a rattle and reached for it. He put out his arms to be lifted up. He screamed when he dropped the rattle and slowly began to be more interested in toys and tried to attract attention. He was propped up in a baby seat and began to watch events in the corridor. He disliked being put on a rug on the floor.

THE SECOND STAGE OF PLAY
Children from about 12 months to 2 years

At this stage the young child will enjoy the new freedom of standing and hanging on to a strong table or chair. He will love to push and pull strong boxes and trucks on wheels or castors. His limbs are in constant use and every day he makes progress in controlling them. He plays with tins, bricks, unbreakable cups, saucepans and anything he can lay his hands on. He loves to shuffle paper, to crumple and tear it up. He does not yet play with other children but sometimes enjoys having them around. Mother provides the security he needs and is the essential refuge when danger threatens. While he is playing he is getting self-confidence. This second stage is short as he progresses from crawling to walking. When a baby moves around he likes to go after something. He moves from one piece of furniture to the next. While he is doing this he is learning about distance, time and space.

Babies 'adopt' a special toy. It may be a golliwog, teddy bear, doll, blanket, shawl or dummy. With wear and tear and constant use it may become battered, dirty and sometimes quite unhygienic but it remains a most precious possession. Mothers know the importance of this exalted relic and would not dream of damaging it, losing it or going on holiday without it. The child uses it for comfort, especially when he feels threatened and should certainly be allowed to take it into hospital, where, however unattractive its appearance, it should be accepted as it is at home.

The child's world expands rapidly as soon as he can walk. As he plays and moves around he is constantly enlarging his experience. In his play he learns to control his body and promote his skills. His movements become more and more sophisticated. Play provides an essential outlet for the expression of his feelings. He is now in a phase of development where physical ability and natural curiosity reach a new peak of intensity. Affection, companionship and the right things to play with are very important if the emotional troubles that sometimes occur during the first two years of life are to be lived through successfully without special attention.[1]

Age about One Year

Development in relation to play	Suggestions for play provision in hospital
Sits well, crawls, pulls to standing and lets himself down. Walks round furniture holding on to it firmly. Walks with one or both hands held.	Opportunities for active play both in and out of cots. If restricted, activities with arms and legs should be encouraged to relieve frustration, e.g. drum and drumstick, rope

[1] See also: *The First Two Years* by Susan Isaacs, C.B.E., M.A., D.Sc., Nursery School Association, 89 Stamford Street, London, S.E.1.

Picks up small objects. Will try to put brick into hole or container.

Drops toys deliberately.

Looks for toys which have gone out of sight.

Points out things which interest him.

Knows his own name.

Babbles all the time.

Understands a few words and commands, like 'come to Mummy!' and gestures.

to pull on, trumpet to blow, etc.

Help with walking by playleader and toys such as 'baby pusher', boxes, cartons and large balls.

He needs strong boxes, tables and chairs to pull himself up with.

Enjoys wheel toys on the floor or on bedtable, large and small trucks and lorries, nesting toys, spoons, bowls, cups, smooth tins and containers of different colours and textures.

Large foam cylinders for clambering over and sitting astride.

Songs, talking and clapping games.

Age about Eighteen Months

Development in relation to play

Very active. Walks steadily, climbs a low stair, throws ball.

Carries quite heavy objects.

Scribbles, builds. Enjoys simple picture book.

Uses 6 to 20 recognizable words.

Suggestions for play provision in hospital

Will make more use of push and pull toys, large balls, etc., will climb on low chairs, etc. May enjoy scribbling with thick crayon or sometimes large brush and paint. Can play with dough or clay but will get very messy unless

Enjoys rhymes, attempts to sing.

Very dependent on adult's reassuring presence, needs constant supervision to protect him from dangers in exploring environment.

carefully supervised (see next section).

Continues to use nesting toys, boxes, bricks, containers, spoons, etc., plays happily in sand but needs supervision.

As much scope as possible must be given to explore an interesting environment.

Mobiles hung from the wall, ceiling or cot side give pleasure and help to stimulate the use of the eyes.

Many attractive mobiles can be made. A crystal pendant, small mirrors or discs covered with aluminium foil will reflect light and scatter reflections across wall or ceiling. These appeal to children of all ages. Mobiles can also be made which jingle together and make pleasant sounds.

Age about Two Years

Development in relation to play

Suggestions for play provision in hospital

Can run. Often runs outside.

Whenever possible, expeditions to gardens,

Climbs on furniture to look out of window.

Walks upstairs.

Follows adults around house and copies their occupations in play.

Pulls a wheeled toy.

Puts bricks in a row to make a train.

Can build a tower of 6 blocks.

Uses 50 or more recognizable words and puts them together in simple phrase and sentence.

Knows his own name.

Talks to himself as he plays.

Asks the names of objects.

Make-believe play is beginning.

Listens to stories and will talk about them.

Demands attention.

Clings tightly in affection and fear.

Tantrums when frustrated but attention easily distracted.

Defends possessions.

No idea of sharing.

Plays near but not often with other children.

Jealous of attention given to others.

grounds, streets, etc.

Opportunities to look out of windows.

Visits to kitchen, bathroom, hospital shop.

Boxes and stools to climb over, etc. Toys on wheels.

Enjoys filling vessels with sand or water, needs careful supervision. Painting and play with dough.

Even a child confined to bed can scribble, paint, use sand, water and dough if the bed is carefully protected with polythene sheets. The younger the child the more carefully the messy play must be supervised. He has less control over his movements so the mess can get out of hand.

Hammer toys, peg toys, dolls, cars, bricks of all shapes and sizes.

Has conversation while playing, e.g. 'This is a big one', 'this is a small one', 'this is a red one'.

He will use domestic play things like pots, pans, cups which are also used at home. He can be talked to about them. This can

Concerned with the present. Past and future have little meaning.

keep his family alive in his mind.

Stories begin to be appreciated as well as rhymes and acting games. Discussions take place with picture books and the making of animal, train noises, etc.

When possible, provide pets, birds, fish, etc. They will be much enjoyed.

Examples of Play with Children in Hospital

Janice (18 months)

In plaster up to her waist, Janice showed great frustration at this immobility. The playleader placed her on a foam pillow on a rug on the floor and she used her arms to get around. She found a miniature golf club and was given two ping-pong balls. This was a huge success, there was plenty of space for Janice to go after the balls with the golf club, she shrieked with laughter. The other children watched enthralled, some joining in. Janice played on the floor in this way every day, sometimes resting, sometimes active. She became a much more contented child and far more communicative than she had previously been.

Tommy (18 months to 2 years)

Socially deprived, living in one room, Tommy was born with a heart defect. He was in hospital for 6 months waiting until he was ready for a serious heart operation. He was missing many of the normal experiences of healthy children. At first his play was sporadic and disjointed and he was often in the way. Everything had to be protected from his marauding hands. Because of this he spent many hours in his cot in a very limited environment. When the playleader arrived life changed for Tommy. He spent much of his day in the playroom or going for walks in the grounds. He was given the usual occupations for a child of this age, and most important, he joined in games, talks and songs. His vocabulary increased rapidly. When he recovered from the operation and was discharged from hospital he did not have many difficulties in adjusting to normal life. It was the fact that the playleader had had time to devote herself to this non-medical care of him that enabled him to bridge the gap between life as an invalid in hospital and a normal childhood at home.

THE THIRD STAGE OF PLAY
Children from about 2½ to 4 years

The child will now be able to run and climb with ease and takes great delight in his physical attainments. Out in the country some two-year-olds will climb along tree trunks with absolute assurance. This climbing confidence in very young children has also been observed in Adventure Playgrounds, demonstrating the skill and enjoyment in accepting a challenge. Harm can be done in restricting the child who feels confident in undertaking daring exploits.

At this age he is always on the move and seems tireless in his active pursuits. He is absorbed in play with 'messy' materials. At the same time he can symbolize in his play the meaning he has discovered in the practical activities he watches in his daily life. Harry, aged 3, was playing in the kitchen while his mother washed the dishes. He grabbed a saucepan lid, sat on the floor and put it between his legs. Grasping each side he converted it into a steering wheel. With puffed out cheeks he made car noises and steered his imaginary vehicle round the floor. As he turned corners he pressed the handle knob and hooted.

Domestic play is freely imitated and indulged in; fact and fantasy are tested, dolls are treated as human beings, telephone conversations are made, cars, buses, trains, etc., are recognized as part of a transport system. Pictures of familiar objects are recognized in books and the child will talk about them and listen to adults talking to him about the events of daily life. In drawing and painting the child begins to express people and things as he 'sees' them—although this is still very different from the way an adult will see and represent them. It is important for adults to help children make their own ideas as vivid and dynamic as possible. Copying and colouring drawings in a book can inhibit their own observations and development. In all creative play it is important to encourage children to express their own fantasies rather than to copy the work of others. Paint, crayons, clay, dough, fabric, egg boxes, cartons and all kinds of bric-a-brac add to the creative possibilities of picture making. Three dimensional pictures and collages can excite a searching mind or encourage hesitant fingers in an outburst of activity.

Messy play with sand, dough, mud, water, clay and paint is an important and universal activity satisfying children at many stages and in many predicaments. Some of the first scientific experiments are made in the bath while splashing, filling and emptying containers. Some things are found to float and others to sink to the bottom. All kinds of discoveries are made with water. Wet things become dry, dirty things can be cleaned.

Messy play also has a therapeutic value because it can be indulged in throughout the period when children are taught to conform to the standards of the society in which they live. Within a short period they are usually taught to eat in an orderly way, to keep themselves neat and clean and not to make muddles in the home. At the same time, toilet training is in progress. Conforming to standards of cleanliness imposes a severe strain on some children and the permission to indulge in messy play helps them to accept these standards. A tense child can often find contentment and relaxation in water play or making mud pies and at the same time it can help in controlling bowel and bladder. An aggressive child can get much satisfaction from digging, building and knocking down mud pies, sand castles and towers of bricks rather than by damaging manufactured toys, so materials of this kind should always be available.

During this stage two children will sometimes play together for a short time and younger children will copy the older ones. Naturally they are not mature enough to share toys and indignation is freely expressed by both when one child snatches a toy from another.

Age about Two-and-a-half Years

Development in relation to play

Suggestions for play provision in hospital

Walks upstairs alone, but holds rail going downstairs two feet to a step. Runs well straight forward and climbs easy nursery apparatus. Pushes and pulls large toys skilfully but has difficulty in steering them round obstacles. Jumps with two feet together. Can stand on tip-toe if shown. Kicks a large ball.

In playroom or ward, boxes and planks to be used for climbing. Planks are useful as can be used in conjunction with chairs and tables— to make slides or for balancing on. Simple games of jumping, stretching, running. A tambourine can be used for clapping, stamping, etc., rhythmically. A child in bed can beat time with drum, wooden spoon or clap and sing and thus

Builds tower of 7 cubes.
Recognizes minute details in a picture book.

Uses 200 or more recognizable words. Talks intelligibly to himself at play concerning events happening here and now.
Continually asking questions 'what' and 'where'?
Says a few nursery rhymes.
Enjoys simple familiar stories read from picture book.

Very active, restless and rebellious.
Throws violent tantrums and less easily distracted.
Emotionally still very dependent upon adults.
Prolonged domestic make-believe play but with frequent reference to adult.

Watches other children at play interestedly and occasionally joins in for a few minutes but little notion of sharing playthings or adult's attention.

join in with the more active children in the ward. Enjoys trucks, carts, pedal cars, large balls, bricks.

Stories, songs, picture books which should portray, if possible, things within the child's experience.

Every effort should be made to encourage movement. A child in plaster can be put on a mobility trolley or moved onto a rug on the floor and given opportunities to bang about with wooden spoons, drums, rattles, etc.
Expeditions beyond the ward whenever possible; use of windows.

Domestic play with toy cookers, washing-up bowls, iron and ironing board.

Dressing up as parents, nurses, doctors, ticket collectors, bus drivers. Children in bed can have fun with hats, masks, capes and jackets. A steering wheel can be attached to the cot.

Paint, finger painting, dough, clay, sand and water play whenever possible.

Natural objects to handle like feathers, cork, bark, shells, potatoes, carrots, etc.

Mirrors and magnets.

Playplax—transparent coloured shapes.

Corners enclosed to make homes and private sanctuaries—large cartons for individual hideouts. Some children seek privacy in large open wards and appreciate a 'corner' just for themselves.

Age about Three Years

Development in relation to play

Walks alone upstairs with alternating feet and downstairs with two feet to a

Provision for play in hospital

Climbing apparatus where possible. Opportunities for physical activities must not step. Climbs nursery apparatus with agility. Can turn round corners while running and also while pushing and pulling large toys. Rides tricycle and can turn wide corners on it.

be overlooked. Expeditions outside ward or cubicle. Activities which involve movement even in bed if physical condition permits, e.g. beating drums, hammering pegs, toy steering wheel, cranes and pulleys. Kicking and stretching games. Balls fixed to bats with elastic. Balloons on strings. Tricycles and pedal cars.

Paints with large brush on easel. Cuts with scissors. Large intelligible vocabulary. Talks to himself in long monologues mostly concerned with immediate present, including make-believe activities. Carries on simple conversations and verbalizes past experiences. Asks many questions beginning: 'What?', 'Where?', 'Who?'.

Cutting out pictures from magazines, especially those with domestic and homely objects. A great deal of conversation can be stimulated by this activity. Individual or group collages and friezes can be made as well as wall charts, scrap books, etc.

Dressing up play, nurses, doctors, mothers, fathers, etc. Domestic play with kitchen utensils—ironing, washing, cooking, sweeping, with dolls. Keeping alive everything outside hospital—links with past and future. Conversations about past and present and events in hospital.

Listens eagerly to stories and demands favourites over and over again.
Knows several nursery rhymes.

A reader will almost always attract a group of children who want to listen to stories and songs. This can often take place at the bedside of a child who cannot get up. Great value in group activity—particularly for children in cots as it helps them feel less isolated. Pull cots and beds into circle for singing together with piano, guitar, recorder or any suitable instrument available. Nursery rhymes can be acted or puppets made to perform the stories and rhymes. A record-player can be used for suitable rhymes, etc.

General behaviour more amenable. Likes to help adults' activities in house and garden.
Makes effort to keep his surroundings tidy.

Likes to use adults' tools— dustpan and brush, hairbrush, razor (without blades!), mirror, garden spade or rake.
Importance of body image. Use of mirror with dressing up. Making handprints, footprints, drawing round body lying on shelf paper.

Enjoys floor play with bricks, boxes, toy trains and cars.

Boards for bed-rest children can be marked out in 'roads' for small cars; roads, rivers, etc., can be

Joins in play with other children.
Understands sharing play things.
Shows affection for younger siblings.

chalked across the floor. Enjoys simple puzzles, construction toys, building games, peg boards.
Sand, water, paint or clay provided for communal play can also be arranged individually for children confined to bed. As much messy play as can be arranged.
A teddy bear $2\frac{1}{2}$ to 3 feet tall provides an excellent target for expressing feelings.

Examples of Play with Children in Hospital

Mary ($2\frac{1}{2}$ years)
This child was a spina-bifida hydrocephalic, paralysed from waist downwards. This active and intelligent girl was wrapped round securely in a blanket from waist to toes and placed on the floor. She quickly used her arms as 'paddles' for moving around. She first approached a bowl of sand on a polythene sheet on the floor and played with the sand sifting it through her fingers and then filling and emptying containers. All the time she talked about what she was doing. She made long expeditions across the ward, picking up things which interested her, such as dolls or bricks. She made her way out of the ward along the corridors and as far as the school and play room. She was like a young seal on dry land, her arms acting as flippers. She explored the whole paediatric department enjoying a chat in the kitchen or watching proceedings in the bathroom. Her chatter and infectious gaiety influenced everyone

within her range. Her own accomplishments improved
rapidly as she was given freedom to move and opportunities for play.

She also had a mobility chariot which she could propel
round the room, her hands turning the wheels. Older
children on tricycles and pedal cars joined her in races
and games of skill.

At mealtimes Mary either sat in a high chair at the
table with the other children or sometimes had her meals
on her bed where she would be helped by nurses or playleader. Wherever she was her spontaneous enthusiasm
contributed to the well-being of the ward.

When Mary was on bed-rest she often had to lie on her
stomach for days. This was tedious but she was helped
by a doll who was given the same treatment. Mary often
admonished the doll and told her to behave herself and
lie on her tummy and it wouldn't last much longer. Mary
and the doll suffered the ordeal together.

Sancho (3 years)

This child 'in for observation', was Spanish and only
knew a few English words. He was very distressed when
his mother left him and it was extremely difficult to comfort him. He was attracted by a brightly coloured ball and
for some time threw it and ran after it. The playleader
began to play ball with him and he relaxed as he began
to play. This was a 'language' he could understand. There
was a Spanish cleaner in the unit and the playleader asked
her to come and talk to Sancho. She was very pleased to
do this and almost every day afterwards Sancho would
follow her with mop and duster and help her polish the
corridor floors. Gradually he became slightly more reconciled to staying in hospital and less tearful when his
mother left him after her evening visits. A bond of trust
and friendship grew between Sancho and the playleader
which he made great use of during his three weeks in

hospital. She helped to fill the gap during his mother's absences.

Errol (3½ years)

This boy had Hirschprung's disease and had been in and out of hospital since birth and had many operations. He had been very ill. He had a colostomy. His parents visited him whenever possible but they both worked. He was very fond of his mother.

The first time the playleader worked in his ward she saw him sitting on a tricycle and he cycled round all day long. He visited the nurses in the office and went to the kitchen. Sometimes he came to see what the playleader was doing with the other children, but during the first week he did not join in.

The first time there was painting he watched but did not want to do it. The second time he wanted to paint. He did it carefully but refused to wear an apron and said he did not want to get dirty. He was told that it did not matter getting dirty as he could always be cleaned up with soap and water.

When his dressings were changed he nearly always cried and obviously disliked the mess.

After the next painting session he asked to clean the brushes in the sink. He continued to enjoy painting and particularly clearing up the painting mess afterwards. One day the playleader and nurse discussed whether he could help to change his dressing and to clean himself up. The nurse welcomed the idea and gradually Errol shared in the nursing procedure and cried less frequently when this was done.

This example shows how a young child can be helped to come to terms with his condition and the contribution which play supervised by a skilled person can make to alleviate some of the problems of illness and treatment.

THE FOURTH STAGE OF PLAY
Children from about 4 to 5 years

Children at this stage will still be using play to deal with all kinds of problems which their limited use of vocabulary prevents them expressing verbally. They will need a great variety of play materials to encourage the skills they are eager to develop. Instead of finding satisfaction in banging about with hammer and pegs they begin to want to learn how to use hammer and nails to construct such things as aeroplanes with three slats of wood.

As well as plenty of opportunities for physical activity more opportunities are needed for constructive and creative play. There will be much more persistence to achieve results and it is important to have these appreciated. In painting and modelling, provided they have had former scope for experimenting, they will begin to leave behind experimentation with materials and start to enjoy pattern and picture-making.

Group play becomes increasingly important. Some children naturally become leaders and others prefer to be the followers. Sand, water play, clay and paint are still among the most popular activities. Dressing-up clothes, high-heeled shoes, shopping baskets and handbags are in constant use. Children join together to play at buses, trains, shops or to go on fishing expeditions. Sometimes firm friendships will develop between two children which may last throughout primary school and longer.

Already preferences for different activities can be observed which may remain lifelong interests. One child will enjoy books and stories, and quiet pursuits. There is often a special story he will ask for again and again. Others will spend as much time as possible out of doors, and some girls will spend more and more time in the home corner with dolls, cooking, shopping and arranging hair appointments on the telephone, etc.

Age about Four Years

Development in relation to play	Suggestions for play provision in hospital
Turns sharp corners when running, pushing and pulling. Climbs ladders and trees. Expert tricycle rider. Hops on one foot.	Opportunities for active pursuits, acting and musical games. Whenever possible use to be made of outside play. Area in ward or playroom to be made available for active games and climbing if possible. Constructive out of doors building with any large material available.
Matches four primary colours.	
In speech shows only a few infantile substitutions. Gives correct account of recent events and experiences. Gives home address and (usually) age.	
Eternally asking questions 'Why?', 'When?', 'How?' and the meaning of words.	Whenever possible honest answers to be given to the innumerable questions. Simple explanations about hospital procedures.
Listens to and tells long stories sometimes confusing fact and fantasy.	Story-telling, singing games. Books on shelves in reach. Hospital equipment

Strong dramatic play and dressing up favoured.

Needs other children to play with, and is alternately co-operative and aggressive with them as with adults.

Understands taking turns.

Shows concern for other siblings and sympathy for playmates in distress.

used in play with dolls, children or adults as patients. Medicines mixed up. Stethoscope, hypodermic syringes, bandages, etc. Dressing up clothes.

The home corner supplied with domestic utensils including two telephones for conversations.
Shops can be made in corners with scales, counter, till, jars or tins filled with dried beans, acorns, pebbles. Paper bags for wrapping up.

A large variety of creative materials for play, paste, scissors, woodwork, clay, dough, water, paint, finger and string painting, sponge painting, potato cuts. Paper of all sizes, shapes and colours.

Boards for dough with rolling pins, pastry cutters, patty pans, etc. When possible 'real' cooking that can be eaten.
Water play with polythene bowls, aprons, a variety of containers, bubbles and bubble pipes.

Sand wet and dry in bowls or on a sand tray. Beds covered with polythene sheets and children in overalls.

Age about Five Years

Development in relation to play	Suggestions for play provision in hospital
Active and skilful in climbing, sliding, swinging, digging and various 'stunts'. Runs lightly on toes. Skips on alternate feet.	Ball games, climbing frame, skipping ropes, skittles, trampoline, rope nets, quoits. Expeditions to park, grounds, shopping, etc., tricycles, dolls prams. Balancing on treacle tins tied together with string. Stilts. Hobby horses, wheelbarrow, garden tools. Steering wheel in bed for immobile child. Musical games, singing games, music and movement. Record player. Band in playroom, ward or in bed.
Dances to music.	
Names four primary colours and matches 10 to 12 colours. General behaviour more sensible, controlled and independent.	
Serial and dramatic play.	Cooking, real and imaginary. Shops. Dressing up alone and with companions. Makes swords and guns. Hospital play. Group games with cards, Snap, Happy Families, etc. Group games with boards
Chooses friends.	
Co-operative with companions and understands need for rules and fair play.	

Plans and builds constructively.

Plays complicated floor games.

Appreciates meaning of clock time in relation to daily programme.

Protective towards younger children and pets.

Comforts playmates in distress.

and dice: Snakes and ladders, Mousie-Mousie, Flounders, etc.
Model making, woodwork, workbench. Paint, felt pens, tie-dyeing, junk collages. Water play, sand, dough.

Jigsaws, Spirotot, construction sets, Lego, Playplax, peg board, Solitaire, marbles, screw toys, torches, mirrors, magnets. Toy farm, zoo, village, garage.

Sewing, weaving, embroidery on rug canvas, cutting out.
Decorating dolls' house, making furniture, doll play, hospital ward.

Pets if conscientiously looked after can be brought into the ward as well as kept in the garden. Bird tables in view of ward windows.

Discussions about other patients. Often an older child will 'adopt' and play with a younger child, to the benefit of both.

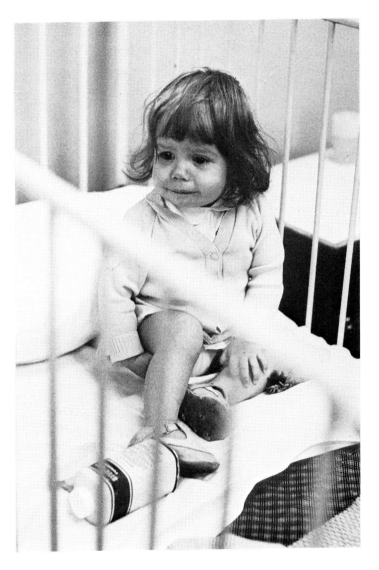

1 Distress

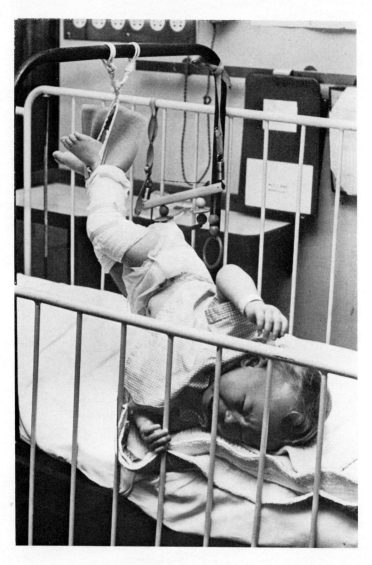

2   Captive and miserable

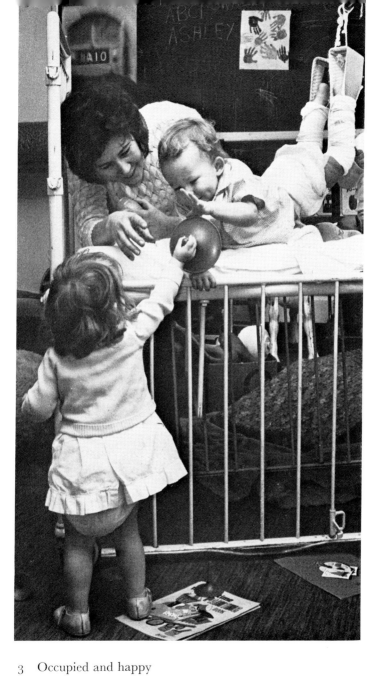

3 Occupied and happy

4 The playleader should be aware that children may wish
to discuss their illness and treatment

Examples of Play with Children in Hospital

Donald (4 years)

He had a broken arm and enjoyed playing almost exclusively with two sets of toys—small cars which he pushed
round on the tray and puzzles. He repeated each puzzle
with his left hand over and over again. It seemed as if he
was assuring himself that he was still in working order.
When he returned to 'out-patients' for a check up he
asked to come up to the children's ward to do puzzles.

Millie (4 years) and Janet (4 years, two months)

They spent most of each morning in the home corner—
'baking' with dough, giving 'tea' to all who would accept
a cup and sweeping the floor. When Millie was discharged
Janet gave up this play and was lonely and lost until she
discovered how to blow bubbles. She played a great deal
with soapy water. The friendship had benefited both
children and had helped them to become reconciled to
hospital life.

Betty (4 years)

Admitted with lead poisoning, she was in the ward for
about three months. She attached herself to any visitors
who noticed her and were willing to take her for walks or
give her sweets. She had little ability to concentrate and
lost her temper when faced with any difficulties in constructive play. The playleader was the 'visitor' who
appeared regularly and was ready to be friendly. She
insisted that the playleader took her to the lavatory. She
would also only play with blocks, pegs, puzzles when she
had undivided attention. She would become tearful and
refuse to eat at lunch time unless she was allowed to wave
'good-bye' to the playleader from the window. When this
ritual was observed she was satisfied and enjoyed her meal.

Betty clearly showed her need for a continuous
relationship with an interested adult. This is particularly

important for children whose parents visit infrequently. Continuous relationship provides consistency in handling which is of the utmost importance to insecure children.

Francis (4 years)
He had severe kidney trouble and was very upset for the complete nine days of his stay. He had to be in bed and would only play when an adult sat at his cot and gave him undivided attention. As soon as he was left he would relapse and lie down in misery.

Six months later he was re-admitted and was contented and cheerful throughout his stay. He played with concentration and imaginative enthusiasm, drawing and modelling on his bed table. Suddenly he referred to his previous stay which he now consciously recalled, and summing up his own progress asked 'Can I play with those pots I played with when I was a baby?'

Sandy (4½ to 5 years)
He had anaemia and cardiac disease and came from a happy, loving family and had four brothers and sisters. He was regularly visited but his parents could not stay for long.

After a week of running around freely he was put on 'bed rest'. He was an extremely active child and seldom felt unwell which made it difficult for him to understand either his lengthy stay in hospital or the need to be in bed. He noticed that other children quickly went home. Every possible physical care was given to him by the doctors and nurses. As a patient he was almost too good and accepted painful procedures with equanimity. He returned elated from a blood test saying, 'I didn't cry. It didn't hurt, I've got used to it now.' At first he was frightened by them. He played a great deal with a disposable hypodermic syringe (needle removed) from the hospital play box.

Throughout the months he remained in the ward he needed additional care to help him accept and understand the lengthy treatment. Sandy showed clearly how maturation and learning in its widest sense can be provided for a normal child in the abnormal setting of a hospital ward. He talked a lot about his life at home and discussed such things as Daleks, knights, dragons, robots, etc. The play-leader suggested he dictated to her letters to his family. He suddenly grasped the idea that this was a way of communicating with them by proxy. He dictated long letters expressing his longing to be home. A great flow of words and ideas resulted from this and another five-year-old began to dictate as well.

At first he refused to paint, saying 'I can't paint, I can only draw'. Then he joined in painting a picture with a friend and suddenly realized he had acquired a new skill of which he was very proud. 'I didn't used to do paintings.' Within a few days he had painted some pictures which showed rapid mastery of a new medium through which he was expressing a very fertile imagination. Similarly with clay, after some guidance and help he made great progress.

He was taught to write and to recognize a few letters and he talked about school. Once he picked up a very difficult puzzle and was warned he might not be able to manage it, but he said firmly: 'I can do it if I concentrate. I've got to learn. I want to grow up, I like learning things.' He completed the puzzle.

When there were only a few children in the ward the playleader was able to give him a great deal of attention and he asked many questions which she was able to answer and discuss with him. 'Why do people die when they grow old?' 'What would happen to me if my Mummy and Daddy died while I was young?' 'Why am I ill and not my brothers and sisters?'

His worries were alleviated by his questions being answered. The fact that he was able to discuss his problems and continue his learning reduced the disadvantages which a long stay in hospital might have had for him.

There are of course children who despite the efforts of all the staff, including the playleaders, do not accept their time in hospital as equably as the children in the examples given here. Children's emotional vulnerability varies very much. Children over about three and a half years of age who have been carefully prepared for a hospital stay are likely to adjust better than younger ones, or those who are suddenly rushed in desperately ill and who may remain unconscious of the change in their surroundings for some time.

(See also the sections on emergency admissions, page 121 and the very young child in hospital, page 93.)

FIVE YEARS OLD
Play Suggestions and Activities

Domestic Play
Doll washing, washing clothes, pegging out, ironing.
Cooking—real and imaginary.
Dough play.
Sweeping and dusting.
Telephones.
Shops.
Tea parties.
Play in Wendy House.

Dramatic/Imaginative Play
Dressing up.
'Hospital Play'.
Soldiers, Cowboys, play with swords and guns.
Acting out stories.
'Ghosts'.
Manipulating puppets.
Play with torches, mirrors, etc.

Play using Manual Skills
Painting—string/sponge/fingers/brushes.
Making collages, friezes.   Crayons.
Clay.   Felt pens.

Water.
Bubbles.
Junk.
Simple woodwork with a work bench.
Cutting out with rounded-end scissors.
Gummed paper shapes.
Embroidering on canvas.

Etch-a-sketch.
Spirotot.
Potato cuts.
Papier Mâché.
Knitting Nancy.
Measuring.
Pasting.

Dolls House Play
Arranging furniture.
Decorating.

Pipe cleaner dolls.
Gypsy Peg dolls.

Musical Games
Nursery Rhymes.
Singing games.
Percussion band.

Music and movement.
Record player.
Musical instruments.

Books and Stories
Picture books on accessible shelves.
Reading aloud.

Construction and Arranging Games
Lego.
Playplax.
Beaufix.
Bilofix.
Plastic Meccano.
Jigsaw puzzles.
Pegboard.
Hammer toys.
Picture Lotto.

Toy village.
Farm.
Garage.
Zoo.
Fort.
Fishing games.
Screw toys.
Boob tubes.

Dice and Board Games
Snap.   Solitaire.
Flounders.   Bagatelle.

Snakes and ladders.
Marbles.

**Games involving physical exercise indoors/
outdoors**
Pulleys and cranes.
Ninepins.
Quoits.

Tricycles.
Pedal cars.
Dolls prams.

Walking on treacle tins.
Ball games.
Hoops.
Inflatable equipment.
Rope Commando net.

Hobby horses.
Climbing equipment.
Slides.
Rope ladder.
See-saw.

Expeditions around or outside the hospital.

Pets

Fish in tanks, birds, hamsters, guinea pigs, etc.

Play Cushion (see Fig. 1)

A play cushion has been designed for children in oxygen
tents when it has not been possible to suspend toys across
the cot. A small foam rubber cushion 16 inches by

1   Diagram of a play cushion

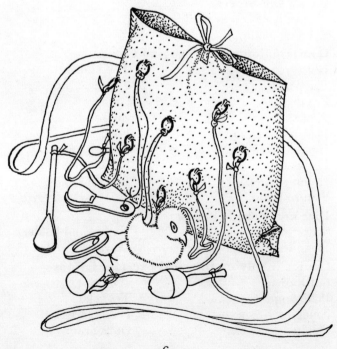

16 inches was covered with washable material. P.V.C. is recommended, 12 strong curtain rings were spaced out and firmly sewn on to the cushion cover. Tapes of varying lengths were tied on to the rings and a variety of playthings attached to suit the requirements of each child using this equipment. The play cushion was found to be useful for a whole range of situations as well as for the child in the oxygen tent.

In a cot it can be wedged between pillow and a baby seat. Alternatively it can be tied with a long tape right round the mattress; when it is firmly tethered in this way it cannot be pushed or kicked so that the attached toys are dispersed and out of reach of the child.

A play cushion can be used on a bed when it is impossible to suspend toys or it can be used on the floor, tied to a piece of furniture. Experience has shown that little children frequently kick or throw toys out of reach and then have nothing to play with. The play cushion is one way of solving this problem.

OBSERVATION OF SIX CHILDREN AND HOW THEY SPENT ONE HOUR, 11 A.M. TO 12 NOON IN HOSPITAL

By Mrs Nora Williams, *Lecturer in Child Development, Southwark College for Further Education*

In none of these cases was it possible for the mother to be present. The children were far from home, or the mother could not leave the rest of her family, or the mother worked in the morning, or did not care to come.

In Hospital A there were qualified playleaders.

In Hospital B play arrangements were left to mothers and voluntary helpers.

In Hospital C there were not at that time playleaders. There are some now.

2 Diagrams to show observations of six children and how they spent one hour, 11 a.m to 12 noon in hospital.

(a) Girl aged 1 year 8 months in Hospital A

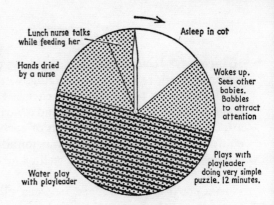

Lunch nurse talks while feeding her

Asleep in cot

Hands dried by a nurse

Wakes up. Sees other babies. Babbles to attract attention

Plays with playleader doing very simple puzzle. 12 minutes.

Water play with playleader

(b) Girl aged 1 year 5 months in Hospital B

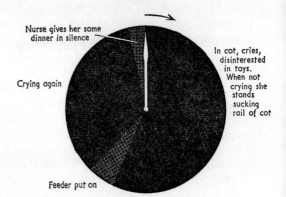

Nurse gives her some dinner in silence

In cot, cries, disinterested in toys. When not crying she stands sucking rail of cot

Crying again

Feeder put on

(c) Girl aged 2 years in Hospital A

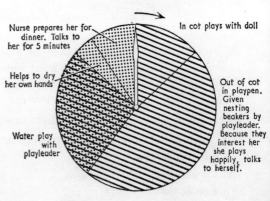

Nurse prepares her for dinner. Talks to her for 5 minutes

In cot plays with doll

Helps to dry her own hands

Out of cot in playpen. Given nesting beakers by playleader. Because they interest her she plays happily, talks to herself.

Water play with playleader

(d) Boy aged 2 years
    4 months in
    Hospital C

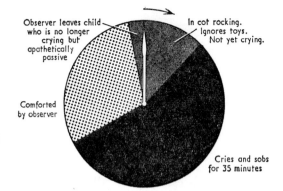

(e) Girl aged 3 years
    6 months in
    Hospital A

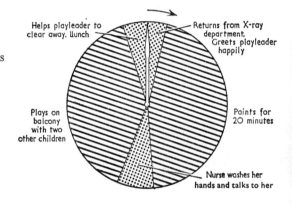

(f) Boy aged 3 years
    10 months in
    Hospital B

Period of sleep

 ıı   ıı apathy

 ıı   ıı crying and distress

 ıı   ıı play

 ıı   ıı social contact with an
          adult

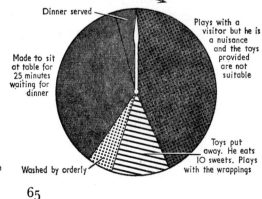

2

Activities and Hobbies
for Older Children (6 to 12 years)

It is essential for all children in hospital to have opportunities to carry on their everyday interests, so that they
can practise their skills, ventilate their feelings, mix with
others sharing similar experiences and spend the long
hours of possibly enforced inactivity in a variety of ways
which have positive value for them. If they are up and
about it is good for them to explore new situations, play
out of doors and make expeditions further afield.

Development in Relation to Play

As stressed in the previous chapter (o to 5 years) it is
important to remember that children pass through the
same sequence of developmental stages but at different
rates. Some of the characteristics of these stages will
influence the way they play.

As they gradually become more independent or revert
to more clinging behaviour as in times of stress or illness
they are sustained by support and guidance from parents.
By about six years old the first phase of childhood is over.
Rapid growth—physical, mental and emotional—has
quietened down. The foundations of personality are laid.
Children are now more adept in the use of words to
describe what they are doing, feeling and thinking. They
can also understand simple explanations about events in
their lives. They have developed a sense of time and are
prepared to wait for things to happen. Since they will have
started school they will have some idea that as well as
belonging to a family they belong to a community.

Children in this age range play vigorously, frequently in groups; they are capable of seeing each other's point of view and accepting a limited amount of defeat. They sometimes play games with rules but frequently the rules are bent to fit individual requirements. Some children relish taking risks, probably knowing they are really safe; they gain confidence in this way and can face up to dangerous situations when they occur. They can be sensitive to teasing, humiliation and failure, particularly when they first meet children in groups away from home.

Accurate observation is beginning and the information collected is discussed and extended in spoken and written communications, in painting and other constructive activities. This provides the opportunity for more formal learning. Imaginative thinking, at this time, is easily stifled unless positively encouraged.

By about seven years old many children have learned to read, write and calculate; they have become established members of school and classroom. They enjoy using their new accomplishments so that word and number games can be added to the repertory. Gang play becomes important and often ends in bruises as one group pits its strength against another. Feelings, sometimes controlled, often break out in howls of rage and derision. One unfortunate child may be picked out for torment and seek protection. Many group activities are marvellously spontaneous and uninhibited. Intellectual interests may be strong and may flourish in their leisure time independently of school work.

Many children welcome some measure of responsibility in family life. They enjoy taking part in discussions on such things as clothes, outings, holidays, choosing meals and treats. Some of them offer to help with house and garden chores, with repairs and maintenance and to go shopping.

Many activities become more organized. For example,

some eight-year-olds will write and produce their own plays. They may form tight neighbourhood groups for football and go on expeditions together which involve camping, making fires and cooking. Others will start collections of stamps, shells, model cars, dolls, etc. As they grow older they come to play games of skill with rules and can accept the idea that each person in the group must have a fair share; taking turns and playing competitively adds to the fun. They often invent their own private games with secret rules; but they will also play games with a strong element of chance such as Snakes and Ladders, where they are as likely to win as their opponent. The urge to conform may become strong.

Around nine years old, some enjoy being responsible for what they do and will often plan and carry out complicated projects with such things as model making or scientific experiments. They can be dare-devils and boast achievements beyond their capacity. At the same time they enjoy talking over their interests with adults and listening to grown-up conversation. As well as playing with other children they may welcome privacy and time to be alone.

As children begin to feel grown-up they choose companions who will share their interests; they become angry when they see injustice done and they begin to question social topics both national and international. Boys often choose to play with boys and girls with girls. Differences in the rate and extent of individual development become increasingly marked.

From eleven onwards childhood is coming to an end and puberty is beginning. Play will satisfy a whole complexity of needs. Some children develop a craze for some activity and work it through to exhaustion. Others let off aggressive tendencies in hard physical exercise or in intellectual games like chess. Interests and skills in arts, crafts and athletics are ways of experiencing deep satisfaction as well as achieving status in a group. What began in childhood as spontaneous play may now emerge as a lifetime interest in art, music, a skill or social service.

Implications of Working with Older Children

In hospital the playleader aims to provide hobbies and activities which can be enjoyed by school age children. She will draw on their experience and provide stimulating materials and pursuits which encourage curiosity. As Dr. Stafford Clark says: 'In the constructive use of the hands to make things even the most unhappy can often find strange peace.'[1]

Children of all ages if sent to hospital can feel small and helpless and will rely on parents for comfort. Some choose toys and games which they played with at an earlier age, as they cannot concentrate as efficiently as when they were well. As they recover, concentration returns, though some will still tire easily. Playthings given to such children should be easy to manipulate and manage. Sometimes schoolchildren will play happily with younger ones but occasionally they will drift away and feel humiliated by being asked to join 'the babies'. A room or cubicle can be provided for them where they can enjoy their books, magazines, record players, etc. In such a way their greater maturity can be given practical recognition.

Separation from the normal environment may still produce its effect upon these older children, but as Mrs Bianca Gordon (psycho-analyst), says, this cannot sufficiently explain many of the emotional difficulties of the child in hospital: 'It is realized that they relate more fundamentally to the actual illness, and to its effect on the particular child, whether he be nursed at home or admitted to hospital.'[2] The playleader should be aware

[1] *Psychiatry Today*. Stafford Clark. Penguin.
[2] *Maternal and Child Care*. April 1969.

that children may wish to discuss their illnesses and treatment as well as taking part in other activities. The child who informs her: 'I've had some blood taken,' may be presenting an opportunity to talk further of the fears of bodily injury, and may be considerably relieved to discuss realities concerning the amount of blood in his body and the tests that will be performed on the sample taken to the laboratory.

Some Examples of Children aged 6 to 12 years at Play in Hospital

Mary (6 years, four months). This child had a skin disease and was many months in hospital; **Diana (6 years)** was in hospital for investigation.

They began to play 'hospital' games, but as they were frequently interrupted by younger children on the ward, the playleader gained permission for them to use the ward bathroom as their 'hospital'. Six dolls were laid in a row and carefully covered with blankets. Mary and Diana sat up to a small table to write notes. Doll (1) called Janet had lost one arm, a drawing was made of her second arm on which was correctly drawn and labelled a scar with 17 stitches. Doll (2) had a stomach scar with 18 stitches correctly drawn and labelled. Doll (3) had 10 scars on her stomach again correctly numbered and labelled. Diana and Mary played this game for two hours on successive mornings. The dolls were washed, fed, given treatment and cared for with accuracy and a sense of responsibility.

Colin (6 years) had had an operation to separate webbed fingers on both hands and was 6 weeks in hospital.

At first Colin had only his thumbs free, so his play was restricted. He used bricks, small cars and the tricycle which he rode round the ward and on the balcony. Messy play was out of the question, but Colin soon became tired of the small range of toys he could use. He wanted to paint, and decided to have a try by holding the brush between his thumb and bandaged hand. He succeeded quite well. Painting held his interest for several days and it was possible to put polythene bags secured with rubber bands over his bandages to keep them clean. It was a landmark for him when the first hand was free of bandages. Although it was his left hand he was able to do a great deal more. The day after his right hand was free Colin went home, he showed everyone his hands—opening his fingers—demonstrating they were no longer webbed. Colin visited the ward when he returned to 'out-patients' and the first thing he did was to show everyone his hands—acknowledging one of the most important events in his life.

Four boys (aged 7 to 11 years), all with kidney disease.
Energetic and lively, they were many weeks on the ward. Two of them, Peter and Harry (11 and 8) formed the nucleus of a gang. They were all affectionate, intelligent and articulate children and arrived on the ward well-behaved if boisterous. It was interesting but sad to see how their behaviour deteriorated. Table manners were the first refinement to disappear. The children watched each other with incredulity to discover the more interesting methods of conveying food to the mouth. They copied each other with great rapidity.

Fighting increased as well as 'soldier' play. Balsa wood was used almost exclusively to make rifles, bayonets and swords with blood-stained points. They grew more aggressive verbally as time went on. Harry suddenly rushed from the see-saw and hit the playleader fiercely and vindictively. He seemed bewildered and upset by the action. This made the playleader realize how essential it was for these sick children to have opportunities for aggressive play.

Luckily a psychiatrist was available and the playleader immediately discussed the situation with him. Many more expeditions were arranged for these children. They were taken to a near-by park where they played on the sand, rolling about in it with great glee—they played football and climbed trees. As the weather was warm the children were allowed to paddle and splash about in the water. Sister never complained about their wet, bedraggled state when they returned to the ward. She encouraged these expeditions and noticed the improvement in the children's attitude to the hospital.

Paul (**7 years**) had a fractured leg from a car accident.

There was no opportunity to prepare Paul for a long period in hospital. He was knocked over by a car when running across the road. The accident happened on Saturday and on Monday when the playleader arrived in the ward she went round talking to the patients and wheeling her trolley stacked with games and toys. Paul said little but chose to paint. Later when the playleader visited him he silently handed her a picture of a street and cars; over one of these was written the word 'car'. He said at once, 'That one knocked me down.' It was the first time he had spoken about the accident. The whole story came out, most of it was in the painting. He had been asked to go and buy a newspaper. A friend went with him. She urged him to cross the road and he ran from the kerb without looking. The doctor and nurses were very interested that Paul had not been able to tell anyone what had occurred until he had had this opportunity to paint. Until that time he had appeared too shocked to speak and had lain silent and withdrawn on his bed. Once he had told everyone what had happened he became friendly and talkative. During the eight weeks in hospital, lying for most of the time on his back, he was able to paint, model, do puzzles and play card games with other children.

Four boys (8 to 10 years) were in a rather crowded ward in a teaching hospital and had been some weeks together and formed a friendship. They had worked through most of the occupations and were bored by the long stay in hospital. They also wanted a place to play on their own and a special game began when they took some toys and played together under a bed in the far corner. They then decided to make a tent—planning it carefully. The basic shape was a large clothes horse covered with a counterpane giving the appearance of a ridge tent. Inside the floor was covered by a mattress. A table was made with books. They were very proud that Sister allowed them to fix an electric light inside. The boys were given their midmorning drinks inside the tent and were allowed to have their rest time there. The Sister and nurses encouraged this game and many of the 'props' were collected by them and the playleader. Because of the confined space in the ward it was all the more remarkable that the tent was allowed to remain for as long as the boys were interested —which was several days.

After this they came to the handwork table and said they wanted to make a Robot. They wanted to make a large one together so the playleader asked them each to make a drawing. Then they discussed the best points of each and made a joint plan. The materials used were cardboard boxes, paper, paste, egg boxes, gold and silver paper. The activity grew, and not only the four boys but everyone—children, staff and parents from two wards— became interested. The Robot took a fortnight to make and when it was finished it was proudly displayed. They all asked how it could be used. 'Let's turn it into a collecting box. Let's collect stamps,' someone said. So one boy made a container to fit inside with an opening in the front and another at the back for emptying. The stamps were collected for a charity and everyone coming to the ward was asked to contribute. The four boys returned home but a new group of children became interested in the Robot. He was repainted and after three months was still a centre of interest in the ward. Moses, one of the original planners, came back for a visit and questions were fired at him about the Robot's construction. Moses was drawn in to helping with the re-painting. Many of the children continued to collect stamps with the Robot and he often featured in their paintings.

Henry (**9 years**) had one leg longer than the other. It was his second visit to the hospital and he may have to return. It was a great advantage for him to know that a play-leader was there and that there were plenty of interesting things to do. He came from Ireland and his parents could not often visit. He was an intelligent and friendly boy. For the first three weeks he had both legs in plaster which reached up to his armpits. He had to be turned over every half-hour; this plus the plaster made play difficult for him. Luckily **James** (**8 years**), a surgical case, was in the next bed and a board was placed between the beds so the boys could play quite well together. When the beds were covered with polythene sheets they were able to paint and blow bubbles. All the same Henry often became restless and he liked to talk endlessly to the playleader about his home and the horses he and his brothers had. He had a scrapbook of photos and press cuttings about the horse shows in which he and his brothers had taken part. In spite of his disability he had won cups and shields. One day he talked about music and said he could play a little. The playleader had a melodica and asked Sister's permission to bring it. Sister was co-operative as usual. Her only proviso was that she should 'have a go' first! The children were very amused when Sister and Staff Nurse disappeared into their room with the melodica and they heard them practising. Henry thoroughly enjoyed the instrument. When he was up he would take it on the balcony and play it really loudly. Other children tried to play it and often groups sang songs to it.

In another hospital there is a large contingent of 'old faithfuls' either in-patients or on weekly visits as out-patients. This helps to make the ward friendly and many long-stay patients form close-knit groups, not necessarily exclusive but fairly intimate. In this ward the children are usually 8 to 12 years old. The ward has a record player which is in constant use. The spontaneous pop group was one of the most entertaining things which this ward has witnessed. One boy lined up all the rubber bins, a toy drum, the pedal-bin and two patella hammers, and proceeded to play drums—with the pedal-bin opening and closing like a pair of cymbals. Other children got hold of tennis rackets and toy guitars and accompanied him. All dressed up in pyjama jackets. The singer of the group got hold of the long rubber plug from the basin and crooned into it. The whole scene was hilarious and uninhibited.

On another day the same children had a very successful action painting group, which included four-, five- and six-year-olds. Paper was pinned up on the wire of the balcony and the children flicked, threw and splashed paint on the paper.

During fine weather all the mobile children made frequent visits to the public playground and made full use of see-saws, roundabouts and slides They played on the stretches of grass and in the shallow paddling pool.

Martin (**10 years**) was a psychological case. He found social contact with the group very difficult. He was a very aggressive and possessive boy and caused endless arguments on the ward. He was fascinated by light, fire and electricity. He had been expelled from school because of setting light to waste paper. While his treatment was in progress the playleader took him alone on a visit to the Science Museum. He was very well behaved on this outing and turned the knobs on many showcases. The friendship of one person and his own interest in the exhibits made this a memorable afternoon. This kind of care helped to channel his dangerous tendencies for destruction into constructive long-lasting interests.

A group of 11 to 13-year-olds played 'hospitals' in a highly organized, secret and private way. The curtains of an empty cubicle were tightly drawn, and for several days no adult was allowed in. Later the playleader was invited to come and see what was happening. Dolls and teddy bears were laid out on trolleys covered with white clothes. Drip stands were set up and used and drip sets were dropping crimson fluid into their stuffing. Enormous injections were jabbed into their chests. Needles had somehow been procured. The patients' notes were carefully recorded:

Teddy —Very high cholesterol in blood.
       4 hrly T.P.R., and B.P.
Dolly —Very high cholesterol in blood.
       4 hrly T.P.R and B.P.
Bear   —Multiple internal bleedings.

Teddy and Dolly had the same illness as many of the children; luckily Bear's complaint bore no resemblance to any child's complaint on the ward. It was said that he had fallen from the window and had been run over by a steam roller. In fine weather the play took place on the balcony with prams and cradles arranged in rows. The children found blood sample phials and test tubes. They concocted vividly coloured medicines with paint which the older ones boiled on the gas stove with scientific fervour.

'Hospital play' is an important activity, particularly

when the instruments actually used in examination and treatment are available to the children, like stethoscopes, hypodermic syringes, dental mirrors, patella hammers, small polythene flasks, bandages and masks; or such things as nurses' and doctors' uniforms—surgeons' caps, shoes, or white shirts cut down for doctors' coats, nurses' caps and aprons.

Some children do not attempt to play out hospital experiences while they are still in the wards. They may have an urge to play in this way when they return home or go back to school. For this reason it is important for them to have at least some medical equipment and dressing-up clothes to enable them to do so. Not only are they going over these important and painful events but they are also expressing their fears and anxieties in a natural way and in some measure becoming reconciled to them.

SUMMARY OF CHAPTERS 1 AND 2

The examples show some of the ways in which play and the playleader can help children of all ages, and in all conditions, whether immobilized in bed or up and active, to deal with some of the distress, pain, anxiety and boredom they inevitably encounter when they are ill and in hospital.

1. Through play they can give expression to their fears, worries and aggressive feelings, their hopes and their efforts to overcome disabilities.
2. They can keep alive their warm and loving feelings for their parents, friends and home, including the image of the everyday world to which they will return.
3. They can continue normal growth and development within the hospital setting.

4. Satisfying play can promote health and happiness and combat boredom on days which feel endless, and help to pass the time until visitors arrive.

5. Confidence can be built up that hospital is not entirely a place of pain and misery. The care of doctors and nurses can be appreciated by older children in curing illness and reducing pain—particularly if hospital is made as friendly, relaxed and homely as possible in its management of children, routines and appearances.

6. Play is a great antidote to the off-putting effect on children of the cleanliness and orderliness in hospital. One paediatrician on his ward round with the medical students, noticing their surprised expressions when they saw the sand and water play on the floor, said, 'The small risk from germs is well worth taking when you see how absorbed and contented they are with this kind of play.'

7. Play helps children feel they are in 'working order', that operations and illnesses have not permanently damaged them.

8. In play friendships are formed and problems shared. An older child may derive pleasure and benefit from caring for a baby or a toddler.

9. Apart from promoting long periods of concentration, a variety of stimulating material provides children with opportunities for learning through exploration and experiment. This intellectual activity gives relief from emotional pre-occupation and natural curiosity is kept alive.

10. Children of all ages, seriously ill or convalescent, can have opportunities to play in hospital whether they are in bed or up. Play can take place in crowded wards or in separate playrooms. There are no valid reasons why play should be withheld from children in hospital.

SUGGESTIONS FOR ACTIVITIES AND HOBBIES FOR OLDER CHILDREN

Creative and Constructive Play

Materials for making things, including woodwork and craft work, bricks, Lego, construction kits, model-making, paint and brushes, paper of different shapes, sizes, colours and textures, waste material, cartons, cardboard, fabrics, dough, wood, glue, nails, hammers, saws, tweezers, pliers, leather punch, scissors, rulers, Sellotape, sewing material, canvas, wools, cane, string, knitting needles, needles, looms; chalk, soap and salt for carving with tools. Materials for tie dyeing, wax rubbing, printing, lino cutting, cooking with pots, pans and cutlery. Origami.

Useful general equipment: trolleys or other containers for sand and water, polythene bowls, waterproof and towelling aprons, polythene sheets for covering beds, tables, floors, etc.

Fantasy Play Material

Dressing-up clothes, lengths of material, home corner, shop corner, hospital play—nurses' and doctors' kits, syringes, stethoscopes, masks, chairs, tables, screens, shadow theatre, dolls' house. This section will also include many ordinary toys such as dolls, teddy bears, tricycles, mirrors, make-up, brush and comb, hairdressing equipment, hose pipe, steering wheel, telephones, etc., puppets and marionettes.

Formal Material

Simple science kits, magnets, batteries and torches, rulers, scales, tape measures, liquid measuring flasks, compasses, graded bricks such as those designed by Dr. M. Lowenfeld, kaleidoscopes, diaries, weathercharts, newsboard, ward newspaper, collections of stamps, etc., writing and letter games, Scrabble, crosswords, projector, tape recorder, telephones.

Dice and Board Games, etc.
Playing cards, Happy Families, chess, draughts, dominoes, Flounders, Snakes and Ladders, Ludo, Spillikins, tiddleywinks, counting games, bagatelle, scoring and working out averages.

In one hospital the playleader arranged 'Bingo sessions' with picture Lotto cards for visitors and children every afternoon. It was so popular that it continued for months.

Music

Record Player	Melodica	Singing
Cymbals	Violin	Songs
Guitar	Harmonica	Pop Songs
Glockenspiel	Triangles	Nursery Rhymes
Pipes	Chime Bells	
Drums	Rattles	

Many instruments can be improvised and made by the children.

Pets
Pets give children an opportunity to show tenderness and care for living creatures. In hospital looking after pets gives them an opportunity for caring for others at a time when they are having so much done for them.

Bird Tables
These have been fixed up on trees in view of the wards. Birds, fish, guinea pigs, tadpoles, stick insects, snails, etc., have been kept on children's wards.

Plants
Seeds, plants and bulbs have been grown in wards and on window sills.

Festivals
Christmas preparations, Easter preparations, celebrating birthdays on the ward.

Physical Activities
Stilts, hopscotch, skipping, shuttlecock, Tenniquoit, table tennis, punchball, climbing apparatus, dancing, scrubbing, hammering, flattening tins with a mallet, ball games, pedal car, tricycle, steering wheel.

Outdoor Games
Verandahs, courtyards, gardens all contribute to the happiness of children in hospital. Walks, even picnics in the hospital grounds or in nearby parks have been undertaken by playleaders with the ward sister's consent and approval.

A hospital playground can be planned on lines similar to the community ones containing sand-pit, water splash or cascade, climbing frame, slide, logs and planks, crates and tyres, tents, garden tools, rakes, spades, buckets, watering cans, sieves, space for little gardens, etc., with seats for children and adults to use.[1] Window boxes have been put up on a ward window sill where plants have been grown and tended by the children.

Books, Comics, Radio, Television
Children in hospital are a captive audience, so a spell in hospital presents a fresh opportunity to read them stories and poetry and to show them attractive books and magazines. Public libraries will often supply and renew books for children in hospital and will advise on a suitable collection for different ages and tastes.

As well as books there are always piles of comics in the wards. Parents are sometimes worried about their value

---

[1] *Planning for Play.* Lady Allen of Hurtwood. 1968. Thames and Hudson.

in spite, or perhaps because of, their popularity. Edna O'Shaughnessy in *Your nine year old*[1] makes some useful comments on why children are fascinated by comics. She suggests that they are read because a child will find in them some aspect of his personality—perhaps depicting his own naughtiness which he is now too old to express literally. Within limits comics even have cathartic value. Superman dominates the pages—that unreal hero to be found in most of us succeeds effortlessly and gives temporary respite to a child's endeavours to reach adult status. In answer to the question, do comics do harm, Mrs. O'Shaughnessy says: 'What is in a comic is already in the children. The comics are a place where they find a "comic" version of either some inglorious or else some unreasonable omnipotent part of themselves. . . . In his comic world some part of the burden of morality and factual necessity is momentarily lifted off the child.' Because a few pernicious comics can be found, parents and others must cast an eye over children's reading material and take action if necessary, at the same time making sure that an alternative choice of books and comics is available.

Those in charge of children must assume some responsibility for what children read, hear on the radio and watch on television. Each child reacts differently and what can be disturbing to one is accepted nonchalantly by another. Watching television can be a passive experience or a stimulating and exciting one. In hospital it is the play-leader's responsibility to select the programmes for the children while they are in her care. Children who are sick, away from home and under stress are more vulnerable to programmes of violence and distress than normally. The same applies to radio programmes although these are not as potentially disturbing as television. The radio can be a

---

[1] *Minibook by Corgi*. One of a series written by members of The Tavistock Clinic, London.

menace if it is left on as a background noise throughout the day. It can blunt a child's capacity for listening and enjoying music and the spoken word in a meaningful and imaginative way. Some children in hospital gain much pleasure from using their own transistor radios to listen to programmes of special interest to them.

Books About Hospitals

Madeline by Ludwig Bemelmans, André Deutsch. Hardback and paperback versions.
A Bit of Magic by Dorothy Clewes, Hamish Hamilton.
The Nurse, Ladybird Series, by Vera Southgate and J. Havenhand, Wills and Hepworth.
Mary Ann goes to Hospital by Mary Cockett, Methuen.
Zozo goes to Hospital by Margaret and H. A. Rey, Chatto and Windus.
The Ambulance by Ann Mari Falk, Burke.
What happens in Hospital by Claire Rayner, Rupert Hart-Davis.

Details of all the above books are given in a leaflet prepared by the staff of the Camden Libraries, St Pancras Library, 100 Euston Road, London NW1 2AJ, called *Smoothing the Path No. 1* available on receipt of stamped addressed envelope from that library.

Notes on Making and Use of Puppets

A puppet can act as a companion for a shy or timid child, or one who has grown too old for dolls. It provides an outlet for a child's feelings and evidence of problems which may be causing trouble. Puppets and marionettes have been used to stimulate speech by speech therapists and to encourage the use of limbs by physiotherapists.

Puppets can be simple or very complicated. A face drawn on a finger nail and a twist of paper for a cap is quickly and easily made on the spur of the moment and one on each hand can make an engaging pair for intimate conversations. A frill of ribbon round the finger can make a skirt. Little animals can be made in the same way. Matchbox lids stand well on fingers and paper faces and heads can be attached to them.

Glove puppets are the ones most generally used and small-sized ones are easily made to fit small hands. A firm coil of cardboard is the base on which it is constructed. The coil is made to fit the index finger. The top of this can be padded and pushed into a nylon stocking on which a face has been simply painted or embroidered and hair can be made of wool. The glove part is easily made from cotton or any other strong material if a paper pattern has first been cut out based on the size of the hand. A child's glove can also be used as a base.

A single puppet or a whole family can be a great asset to the hospital toy cupboard. Older children will sometimes improvise a stage and invent their own Punch and Judy shows to entertain the other children in the ward.[1]

Doll Play

In recent years a dolls' house game has been used and developed to observe how children feel about the situations in which they find themselves, and how they feel about the people concerned with their care. As well as a dolls' house a miniature ward can be made up in a suitable box with dolls' house furniture, beds, chairs, tables, lockers, washbasins, bath and w.c. Small dolls represent doctors, nurses, parents, brothers and sisters and the young patients. Playing this game can be valuable as a therapeutic activity and as a means of finding out where a child's particular emotional difficulties lie.

---

[1] Educational Puppetry Association, 23a Southampton Place, London, W.C.1.

Miss Eva Noble in her book, *Play and the Sick Child*[1] writes with much detail and understanding of the observations she made during a special study. Conversation and play were carefully noted on the spot and analysed later. Most of the children assumed the dominant roles; for instance, it was the nurses who were put to bed.

Geoff (**5 years, 9 months**) had not been in hospital since he was four years old. He at once heaped the bedside lockers one on top of the other, made the 'doctor' climb laboriously to the top and knocked all from under him; then picked him up and put him to bed saying, in a gloating voice, 'Now he's got to have an operation.' Jane, on the other hand, thrust the 'nurse' into a cot and said, 'Now you stay in there, I'm fed up with you.' Geoff imposing hospitalization on the doctor, and Jane disciplining the nurse, are typical of the role-reversing performance through which children play out their hospital experiences. In these observations the children themselves demonstrated their needs very clearly. Ways in which these needs might be met were also clearly shown.

---

[1] *Play and the Sick Child.* Eva Noble. Faber and Faber, 1967.

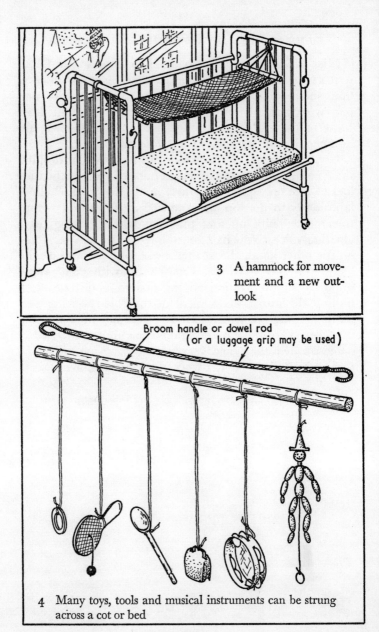

3 A hammock for movement and a new outlook

Broom handle or dowel rod
(or a luggage grip may be used)

4 Many toys, tools and musical instruments can be strung across a cot or bed

5 Peg families and animals for company and games to hang across the cot

6 Mobiles, handmade or bought create a landscape

7 Music can be provided for all ages, especially for children in isolation

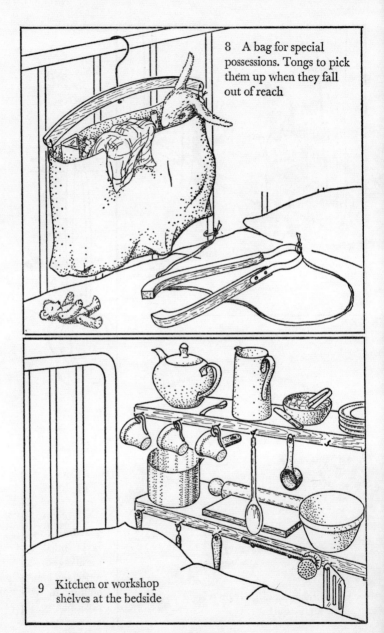

8 A bag for special possessions. Tongs to pick them up when they fall out of reach

9 Kitchen or workshop shelves at the bedside

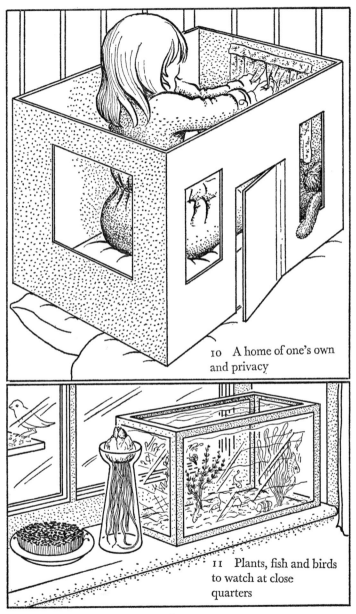

10 A home of one's own and privacy

11 Plants, fish and birds to watch at close quarters

89

12 An improvised punch ball suspended overhead

13 Telephone conversations reduce loneliness and help new friendships

14 Friendships develop as toys and messages are exchanged

15 Simple and elaborate bed tables and trays to make play possible

16 To be on the move opens up new fields for exploration

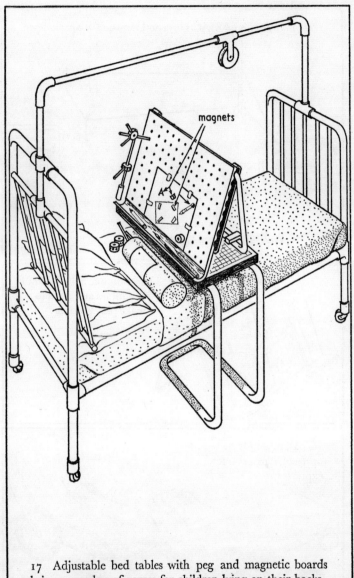

magnets

17 Adjustable bed tables with peg and magnetic boards
bring a number of games for children lying on their backs

3

Children with Special Problems

Introduction

There are certain groups of children in hospital who present special problems and whose welfare and play require specialized attention. These include the very young who are unable to speak fluently or to understand the spoken word, 'long-stay' children, children in isolation, socially deprived children, psychosomatic patients, 'unattractive' or 'repellent' children, children in an eye hospital, accident and emergency admissions.

Many of these children need exceptional care and help, particularly if their parents are unable to visit them frequently as often happens. Some unhappy children belong to more than one of the above groups, e.g. a socially deprived child in an isolation hospital.

The Very Young Child in Hospital

The care and handling of very young children is dealt with in detail in Chapter 1, pp. 29–36. It must be emphasized that children in this age group have first call on the playleader, unless she is faced with an emergency.

Long-stay Children

Many of the problems of 'long-stay' children are common to all children in hospital, but a long stay in hospital brings its special problems.

A child separated from his normal environment for a

long period is in danger of losing his identity as a member of his family, of his school and of the community; he is in danger of missing normal life experiences, riding on trains and buses, shopping, playing in the park, and of interacting with the community at large. He may miss many opportunities for adventure and exploration and suffer from lack of mobility. He may miss the stimulation and competition of being educated with his peers.

The language development of the child who spends some time in hospital may be affected because of poverty of experience (see p. 95). His pattern of life changes, he misses the warmth of family life and many of the opportunities experienced by healthy children to develop emotionally, intellectually and socially in their everyday lives. Hospital names and terms are substituted for family names—he may know all about what a nurse does and forget about the milkman and the postman.

He suffers too from being handled by a constantly changing staff. At home one or two people are in constant touch with him. In hospital he has a number of remote contacts who handle him intimately but fleetingly. There is rarely one person with whom he can develop a warm relationship.

Children in long-stay hospitals are usually physically or mentally affected. Educational and recreational programmes should be planned with these problems in mind. The pre-school child has not yet received the same amount of consideration or provision as the school age child—particularly in hospital—despite the growing recognition of the importance of the early years.

Movement and bodily activity, so important in children's development, is often severely restricted, especially in an orthopaedic ward. Life in a cot can become a world behind bars unless great efforts are made to mitigate this. These children can be put on mattresses on the floor where they can play more easily with other children. If they are securely placed on trolleys they can get some feeling of independence by moving themselves around. If they cannot manage this they can be pushed by adults in the ward, the corridors and outside into the hospital grounds, or into the streets. Cots can be moved so that children can play with each other or listen to stories or music in groups. Small immobilized children need to be taken out of their cots and carried round to see and touch things and to talk about them. Those who must be entirely restricted in plaster or on traction need the stimulation and experience of finger play, action songs and nursery rhymes, musical toys such as drums, dressing up games, as well as interesting construction toys, to use the limbs which are free.

Experience at the Royal National Orthopaedic Hospital at Stanmore shows that mobility stimulates speech.

Ricky (3 years) was retarded both in speech and play. He had spent nearly all his first eighteen months alone in a hospital cubicle, his parents had only been able to visit once a week. Both speech and ability to play with concentration improved rapidly once he was put on a mattress on the floor to play with other children. Water-play seemed to be particularly releasing for him.

Garry (3 years), who was heavily handicapped with multiple deformities and whose speech development was very poor, became positively voluble once he was given a trolley on which he could get around with incredible speed and dexterity.

Richard (4 years), not speaking, was thought for a time to be autistic, but when he was put on a mattress on the floor inside the Wendy House he rapidly developed his powers of speech, if only to order attendant adults to play postman or deliver milk, bread, etc.!

95

'House play' is extremely valuable for 'long-stay' children. A Wendy House, or a light, manoeuvrable, compressed cardboard house[1] which they can easily lift and place over themselves gives them the pleasure of being in a small enclosed space all their own. It is home-like and secure in contrast to the open ward. It satisfies that desire for a secret place so strong in many children and so lacking in hospital. Home corners can also be made on shelves at the level of the patient's bed. A beautifully equipped kitchen was provided for a child on traction in this way—mixing bowls, egg whisk, egg-timer, frying pan, sieve, vegetable rack and vegetables were some of the many things provided for a child whose activities were severely limited.

For 'long-stay' patients domestic play has the additional value of helping them maintain a link with home, keeping alive in their minds the place they have come from and to which they will return. Small children can be given the usual domestic articles such as unbreakable cups and saucepans that they would enjoy as playthings at home, and by talking about them the playleader can help a child go on using ordinary domestic and family words in the hospital setting.

Sally (2½ **years**) in hospital for fifteen months, was visited daily by her mother, who took a great interest in her activities. Sally was particularly fond of 'baking' and mother took home her 'cakes' each evening to cook, bringing back a more edible batch the next day for Sally and her friends to eat. No matter how skilfully he is dealt with in hospital and no matter how inadequate in some cases the home may be, that is where the child belongs and where he will eventually return. If, unfortunately, he is

---

[1] See Figs. 3 to 17, pp. 86–92 for drawings of toys for immobilized children.

from a Children's Home, then it is most desirable to maintain the same contact with that background.

Personal possessions mean a great deal to all of us and this is especially true of the child in hospital who will need a private place in which to keep his belongings. While he is there hospital is a child's whole life and the longer he stays the more he feels that the things in his locker are the only ones in the world that really belong to him.

The following example shows how important these possessions can be.

Steven (**4 years**) had been in the ward for three days for investigation. He was standing on his bed, crying, when the observation began. On his bed there were three books, some biscuits, Potato Crisps, lollies, and toilet articles.

10.45 a.m. Wraps sweets in a piece of paper—puts them in his pocket—sits and whimpers.

10.50 a.m. Stands, tying his dressing gown cord and putting his books inside his dressing gown above it. Books drop out and he puts them back again together with sweets, biscuits, etc., from his bed. They drop again.

10.55 a.m. He tears a page from his painting book and uses this to wrap up his biscuits and sweets, whimpering all the time. Stands up again and stows away his goods once more around his body inside his dressing gown. A young doctor goes to talk to him but gets no response. The teacher comes and tidies biscuits and sweets from his bed into his locker. He allows her to do this but—

11.05 a.m. Whimpers and removes all as soon as she goes away.

Children living in average home surroundings naturally acquire a vocabulary of several thousand words before reaching school age. Research and experience have shown[1] that it is difficult to become verbally articulate if opportunities for speaking, and hearing speech, are not freely available in the early years of development. In many institutions there is not enough emphasis on informal conversation and children become accustomed to words being used only to give instructions or commands.

Children in long-stay hospitals may have limited vocabularies because of lack of opportunity for normal conversation about everyday events and interests.

As well as presenting a wide range of stories, rhymes and songs in dramatic and stimulating ways, the playleader must make opportunities for intimate and informal chat and play with long-stay children—time when they can be alone with her, or part of a small group with her for a cup of tea, a shampoo and set, or a discussion of favourite hobbies. A story read with an individual child gives him that special attention he needs from time to time. Simon, a very insecure four-year-old, used to say whenever his nurse or playleader went to see him: 'Undo the gate (cot side) and come and sit really close and talk to me.'

It is important to provide hand mirrors, or looking glasses at child's height in hospital, otherwise children have no idea what they look like. Another way of counter-acting his confusion is to take hand prints, foot prints, even to draw round his whole body as he lies on paper. Billy, being carried around by his nursery teacher, touched her eyebrows and asked: 'Has I got them?' He was delighted when taken to a mirror and shown that he had indeed 'got them'. 'Dressing up' apart from the pleasure it gives,

---

[1] *Children and their Primary Schools*. Plowden Report, Vol. 2, Appendices 3 and 4.

is an excellent excuse for parading in front of a mirror. Another favourite exercise is to try on an adult's spectacles and see the result.

Music, apart from its therapeutic value, has the power to draw patients, staff and visitors into a group. In one hospital ward where the teacher plays a guitar, what begins as a group activity for children, invariably attracts a large number of patients, nurses, orderlies, porters and medical staff who join in the fun.

The value of handling sand, water, dough and clay has been pointed out elsewhere. Amongst other things this early experience is a fundamental factor in later mathematical and scientific thinking. It is difficult to remember how much the normal youngster learns from daily life. Long-stay children must be provided with experiences and activities to make up for the daily explorations and discoveries they are missing while they are in hospital. They need to be given a variety of objects to count, sort, weigh and measure, to compensate for the lack of normal life experience of quantities.

One of the particular problems of children in long-stay hospitals is the frequency of re-admission.[1] If the child can take away a happy memory of play and friendships, or a more tangible reminder in the form of something

---

[1] Extract from a letter written by the mother of an orthopaedic patient to a hospital:

'I should like to thank you and your colleagues for helping Michael to overcome his fear of hospitals and making his short stay a happy one. Although the surgeons decided to postpone his operation until he is older I am sure his time in the ward has reassured him that hospitals have kind people in them who give them some fun, and he has actually volunteered to go back to hospital when the time comes; I hope he does not change his mind!

'He is thrilled to bits with his clay bowl he made with your help. I have varnished it for him and I am sure he will always associate it happily with his hospital stay. I am sure he has been helped a lot psychologically if not physically!'

handmade, then the fear of re-admission may be reduced. Some children look forward to their return visits.

Finally, by encouraging them to start to move about on trolleys, to take part in handwork, to join in musical activities, the playleader is helping them to develop a sense of independence and a feeling that they are members of a group with a positive contribution to make to everyone else's enjoyment as well as their own.

Children in Isolation Units

Children in isolation are particularly vulnerable, they are not only away from home, but they are placed in a cubicle in solitary confinement. They need to be convinced that this is not a form of punishment. The playleader must give each child as much attention as possible and make sure that suitable playthings are available in each cubicle so that he can occupy himself when she cannot be there. To follow the techniques of barrier nursing the playleader will have to wear a separate gown for each child. The gowns could be of many different colours in order to bring gaiety and informality into the isolation units. Sometimes a mask has to be worn.

In such units there are children of all ages with different infectious illnesses. The cases mainly dealt with are: dysentery, whooping cough, tuberculosis, chicken-pox, measles, broncho-pneumonia, typhoid, infectious skin diseases and gastro-enteritis. They have to be isolated to prevent the spread of infection.

Children from institutions such as Children's Homes, or living in deprived circumstances are more liable to contract infectious diseases. These already unfortunate children are all the more vulnerable when they are isolated. Sometimes they are not visited. Occasionally, the hospital has to ask the police to inform a family that a child is ready to go home. These children have even greater need of care from the nurses and playleaders than those who are in open wards with unrestricted visiting.

When treatment necessitates isolation, children cannot mix and play with others, nor do they benefit from the visitors coming and going in open wards. This means playing alone and losing the stimulation and benefit of group play. It reduces possible occupations, especially for older children who are unable to play competitive games, or those which need more than one player. Enthusiasm which may have been evoked by the playleader tends to wane sharply when she leaves the cubicle. When there are a number of children being nursed in cubicles more play-leaders are required.

Ways and means should be found to reduce loneliness, silence and a sense of solitary confinement. The windows in isolation cubicles should be low enough for the children to see through, and should be made of clear, not frosted, glass. Sometimes children of similar ages can be given adjoining cubicles. Ingenious ways can be arranged for them to make contact with each other. A two-way battery operated telephone will enable them to talk to each other. They could be encouraged to draw and paint on the glass partitions, write messages, play question and answer games, noughts and crosses, etc., using felt pens. These can easily be wiped off when the games are finished.

Sometimes children have dressed up, mimed and acted to each other through the glass. They have made masks and hats, becoming in turn actors and audience. Puppet shows have been given by one child to entertain patients in five nearby cubicles, and this has led to other patients making puppets, some extremely simple, others more elaborate. A puppet often acts as a companion to a lonely child, especially to one who has outgrown dolls. Long conversations have been observed to take place between them. These acting games have sometimes been hilarious;

fun and laughter have permeated the unit drawing in the nursing and domestic staff.

Other children have the advantage of enjoying radio and television, which should be encouraged. Some bring their own transistor sets into hospital. A telephone trolley as used by adults in hospital would be a boon to children. Successful experiments are being made with internal, plug-in telephones, with which children in different cubicles can talk to each other.[1]

Record players and tape recorders are a delight to children of all ages, and the playleader can help to make the fullest use of them. Simple musical instruments such as rattles, drums, pipes, guitars and glockenspiel can help to dispel the silence. Mobiles which tinkle, sparkle and cast beams of light break up the monotonous uniformity of each cubicle.

Because of the risk of infection each child in a cubicle is provided with his own supply of toys which remain with him throughout his stay in hospital. Additions and changes can be made to develop and encourage his interests. When the child is discharged the toys he has had will have to be scrubbed and put into the fresh air, or autoclaved before they can be used again. This means more equipment and storage space must be provided than in ordinary wards. Greater discrimination is, therefore, necessary in choosing equipment as some will have to be destroyed, or be able to withstand sterilization. In a few cases all paper and cardboard books must be burnt. Books and board games can be covered with transparent adhesive material so that they can be scrubbed. Polythene bowls should be provided to give younger children sand or water play in their cubicles. Simple climbing apparatus can also be provided for this age group.

The playleader should always try to keep the child in

---

[1] See Fig. 13, p. 90.

touch with the outside world. Time can be spent looking out of windows, watching traffic, counting cars on the road, or in the car park, talking about the streets, shops, trees, gardens, etc. She may be able to take a child outdoors where plants and leaves can be collected and brought into the ward. Bulbs, plants, mustard and cress, can be grown. There are letters to be read or written to parents, brothers and sisters, and classmates.

An Example of Play in Isolation

Play was especially helpful to **Mark** (**4 years**) whose mother found him unmanageable as he had temper tantrums when she tried to prevent him from doing dangerous things like crossing busy roads on his own.

He arrived in the isolation ward shaking with fright. He was suffering from a skin disease which had erupted in ugly weeping sores. In bed he was propped up on pillows but he was afraid to move because the sores stuck to the bedclothes.

He told the playleader that he liked playing with cars and listening to stories. He busily shoved cars across a tray when she gave these to him and began to feel more comfortable. The game continued while the bed was re-made and the dressings changed. Because of his temper tantrums the junior nurses spent as little time as possible with him, but the playleader found he became deeply absorbed in his play and she could often maintain his interest during the nursing procedures.

Mark became more relaxed and the nurses appreciated the contribution which the playleader made to his care and they asked her to be present when he needed their attention.

With treatment his physical condition improved and this was reflected in his play. He was talkative and positively enjoyed the cars and a toy gun with which he 'shot' everyone in sight. He asked to paint and had his own way of getting satisfaction by tearing the paper into minute pieces and painting each one separately.

Even with ample play arrangements, children in isolation may become destructive both with playthings and with hospital equipment. With ingenuity the playleader will need to devise special occupations to allow these children to let off steam safely, and to make up for boredom and loss of human contact. Her physical presence can mean a lot even to boys of eight to twelve years old who would normally spurn the idea of sitting on an adult's lap. After two or three days of 'solitary confinement' they will jump at the chance of sitting on her lap, playing hand games or having a romp.

Socially Deprived Children in Hospital

Among the children in hospital there are those who are deprived and neglected—this may have been partly responsible for their admission. Some come from homes with baffling social problems, others are admitted because of overt cruelty. Such children have to cope not only with illness but with adversity as well, and to them hospital may be a haven of care and comfort. Here they may find reassurance and help.

Valerie (2 years) was admitted because her mother had purposely burnt her finger tips and hit her on the head with the sharp heel of a shoe. Valerie's mother was eighteen years old, nervous and quick tempered. Valerie was at the stage of exploring everything. The gas cooker had a special fascination for her. The mother made up her mind: 'to give her a lesson she wouldn't forget'. Afterwards, the mother was full of remorse for what she had done and admitted that her temper had 'got the better of me'. She did agree that in future she would take Valerie regularly to the Welfare Clinic, and she felt that this support would help her in the control of her temper. In hospital Valerie spent much time on the playleader's lap or being carried around in her arms. She made a point of helping Valerie at meal-times as she could not use her hands and needed help.

Larry (2 years) had frequent attacks of asthma which were usually brought on by seeing his parents fighting. He was often in hospital.

Nell (8 years) was knocked down by a car and spent ten weeks in the ward, much of the time on traction. As soon as she returned home her mother decided to go away for two days, leaving Nell in the care of a father who was at work all day. Nell played in the street, and three days after returning home, was knocked down by a car, fracturing her leg in two places, and so went back into hospital and was on traction for another ten weeks.

There are children who are under continual stress or are accident prone. They unknowingly court danger and personal injury as if to draw attention to their private miseries. No children's ward is long without a tragic case of this kind. The whole ward team—doctors, nurses, auxiliary staff and playleaders—need to work together to help these children and it may take weeks or months to increase their confidence. Sometimes an abrupt gesture or a sharp tone will induce a state of panic and confusion.

Tommy (2 years) was admitted because his father, having hit him across the face, caused the loss of sight in one eye. The health visitor reported that the father often came home drunk and became very angry if the child cried at night. He refused to allow the mother to go to him. In hospital Tommy flinched when anyone approached him. It took hours of companionship and skilful play before he responded to the playleader or the nurses. For several weeks his activities were disjointed and haphazard. He played destructively and chose things he could bite and tear up. He certainly appeared to be working through some of his hostile feelings. At times, however, he was affectionate and moved his hands lovingly over the play-leader's face, and snuggled up in her arms. He remained several months in hospital until a suitable foster mother was found. She came to see him on the ward and he visited her home with the playleader and medical social worker before he went to live there.

There are children from broken homes and unstable backgrounds. Outside hospital these children are difficult to manage as teachers and welfare workers well know. They can be over-active, aggressive, abusive and destructive. Some are jealous of the attention given to other children, some are excessive in their demands, others are mute and cowed. Some will lie, cheat and steal. In hospital these children may behave in the same way or even worse. Accidents and illness can make them difficult to nurse, especially when parents are not, or cannot be, co-operative. Sometimes the staff's goodwill is stretched to the limit, but it is important to remember that these are the children most in need of special skill and help. Usually their stay in hospital is too short for them to get any real help with their long-standing difficulties. But it is important for them to have the experience of people who are ready to help them.

Many of these deprived children are found in hospitals in overcrowded and dilapidated areas of large cities. The hospitals are often oldfashioned, look forbidding and have shortages of doctors, nurses and domestic staff. This militates against the children's welfare. Although there are many excellent and devoted sisters and nurses their work is hampered by frequent staff changes. A number of trainee nurses come from overseas—strangers to western culture with personal problems of adjustment and language difficulty in the early stages of training. It is not easy for them to understand what the children say, or how they behave. Ill children become frustrated when they are not understood. It is unfortunate when a deprived child, already burdened with social disadvantages, is treated with a standard of hospital care that leaves much to be desired.

The work of playleaders in these wards is quite different from that in teaching and children's hospitals, becoming, as they often do, 'guide, philosopher and friend' to the nurses, parents and children. Nurses in these wards sometimes are less aware of psychological disturbances. They may learn from the way the playleader works how the children can be handled humanely and effectively.

In one 'twilight' area in London there are six Save the Children Fund neighbourhood playgroups and one in the local hospital, with co-operation between them. Playgroup children admitted to the hospital are visited by staff they know—particularly important when parents do not visit. Playgroup staff can provide relevant background information for the hospital staff. On one occasion a girl, aged 3, was knocked down by a van. The parents blamed the child and swore she was never allowed out alone. Everyone concerned with the family knew only too well that she spent hours on the streets. The parents were warned that they would be reported if the child was seen wandering about alone in future.

In this hospital there is a high proportion of road accidents and burns from paraffin stoves in overcrowded rooms. The medical care is of the best, but little thought was given to the children's welfare until a playleader was appointed. The provision of play facilities now keeps the children happy, busy and relaxed. The friendliness and informality of the playroom has transformed the ward and provides a sanctuary for lives scarred by deprivation. It is a widely appreciated service.

Children with Psychosomatic Disorders

Play helps children release tension and cope with everyday stresses. They have to learn how to deal with strong feelings—love, hate, aggression and guilt. A young child is in a sorry plight if he cannot in part canalize his energies in acceptable outgoing ways. Messy play with sand and water, building and knocking down bricks, kicking and throwing balls, chasing games, rough play with small toys, the harsh games of mother and father, school and hospital, are part of learning to manage feelings.

Children with physical, environmental or personal difficulties may not be able, or may not have dared, to externalize in this way, and are consequently impoverished in imagination, initiative, concentration and self-expression.

Children normally go through this stage naturally, but these disturbed children need to have their 'free play' strongly encouraged, if they are not to lose out in their emotional and spiritual lives. What the adult may be able to do through talking, art and music to work out his problems, the young child does through play. After a severe shock or serious illness the resumption of play is indicative of recovery.

In one children's unit for psychosomatic disorders play facilities have been provided. The children are mostly suffering from tension states, psychosomatic and emotional disorders, enuresis, encopresis, asthma, tics, mild behaviour and speech difficulties and some are physically handicapped. They are often anxious and insecure, cannot concentrate or co-operate, and do not enjoy life or make normal progress. In addition to the drugs and other therapy provided by the paediatricians and psychiatrists, the unit aims to provide a stable, interesting and 'caring' atmosphere. An important part of this scheme is the imaginative use of indoor play and an adventure playground.

There is also a playgroup for about 24 pre-school children who attend for a few hours a day; the hospital provides transport and lunch and without these facilities many of the children would have to be in residential care. The children are free to choose their own activities and can play out their difficulties as normal children do, although the playleader is often more involved than in normal play. It is only with insight and close observation that the staff can see what processes are at work and discuss them with matron and the medical staff.

Examples
Helen (2 years, 9 months) had speech difficulties. She was a little whirlwind and could climb as well as any of the big boys. She played with everything, snatching toys from the other children. Her voice could be heard all over the playroom and it did not seem to worry her that nobody could understand her. Within a year there was improvement in her speech and some co-operation with other children.

David (4 years) with retarded emotional development, attended the playgroup for twelve months with little improvement. He had both physical and emotional problems. He had a bad effect on the rest of the group, continually distracting them from communal and creative play, and demanding constant attention to keep him occupied—as he was incapable of thinking for himself. The leader had to bear in mind the needs of the group as well as David's demands. She often asked her assistant to look after the group while she devoted herself to guiding David's activities so that he had a chance to 'play out' his problems without unduly disturbing the rest of them.

Rhona (5 years) was retarded and had speech difficulties. She was one of a large family and her parents, who could not manage her at home, wanted her placed in residential care. They agreed to send her to the playgroup where she spent the morning, had lunch and was taken home in the afternoon. The arrangement worked well and as she improved in her behaviour they no longer pressed for residential care. Her speech improved by leaps and bounds as she met and played with other children, and was encouraged to talk by the playgroup staff. At first she wandered about most of the morning just looking and touching things. This 'inquiring-only' attitude was as far as her play progressed during the first few months. Later she used simple toys constructively and as she was physically strong, a few extra sturdy toys such as hammer, pegs and a baby-walker were especially made for her, and were also used by other children in the unit.

Children who may seem inhibited when they arrive soon become outgoing, noisy and destructive, as they feel reassured and safe in the playroom, with plenty of space out of doors—trees to climb, rope ladders, old tyres, and a large sandpit. Activities like building boats out of crates, using bicycles fearlessly, helping with the gardener's bonfires, chasing games with sticks and guns, are all ways of expressing aggression and learning to cope with fears and with authority. But there are also other less obvious ways.

Doreen (7 years) an enuretic, was afraid of spoiling her pretty frocks. She played for several weeks in a quiet stereotyped way in the Wendy House—then gradually from within the house was heard the most blood curdling treatment of the dolls—'Wet again! I promise you, I'll whip the hide off you if I have to wash those sheets again tomorrow.' Her mother was not as harsh as all that, but the dread of her disapproval was evidently great. Nobody commented on her violent doll play, and gradually she became easier and also more animated and outgoing. Her play became more normal and controlled—and so did her bladder!

Whilst the value of messy play for toddlers is well recognized—enabling them through their free expression to overcome their inhibitions—it is not always realized that it can also be helpful for older children who need to go through some stages of regression.

Tom (**13 years**) with a depressive illness, was highly intelligent. His home standards were obsessively high. He was asked to do some watering in the garden to enable him to behave at a younger age level and to play with water without losing face. He spent many long summer evenings with the hose, splashing it about on the walls and roofs, chuckling, laughing and talking. No one who overheard him could have doubted that he was 'playing-out' his feelings—probably concerned with his excretory functions.

Plasticine and modelling clay also offer good opportunities for 'regressive' play. It is gratifying for a child who has been indulging in faecal play to begin to play with clay. Robert (9 years) carried pieces of clay about in his pocket, frequently playing with them and turning them into little rolls, with a steady improvement in his toilet habits. In painting also, especially with finger-paints, similar phases can be seen if there is a little direction and no adverse comment.

Playing in old cars seems to be a particularly useful game for boys. They can sit at the wheel and indulge in a fantasy about this most masculine of modern activities which helps them with their feelings of defiance, fear or jealousy of their fathers.

Running such a playgroup presents the staff with many difficulties. A variety of indestructible play materials and spacious grounds contribute to the effectiveness of the work, but it is the capacity of the playleader to welcome each child as he is with understanding and tolerance and guide him with consistent care which will make progress possible. It can often be a long process with little reward for child or staff.

The Unattractive or Repellent Child

There are some children in hospital who are unattractive or even repellent to the hospital staff. They may be both unloved and unloving. When a member of the staff tries to make contact she may well be met by a storm of unremitting tears, and it will take courage and a sense of duty to persist in attempting to establish a rapport with such a child. It is important for the staff to recognize their own feelings of distaste for these unlovely children.

Once such a child begins to respond with an occasional smile the adult may begin to find him less repellent and even appealing. The child reciprocates, feeling more loved and wanted, he smiles and responds increasingly and becomes more likeable to everyone in the ward.

Maria (10 months), daughter of inbred Sicilian parents, was described by the playleader as: 'a very ugly child with a thatch of black hair, enormous cauliflower ears, a sunken shrivelled face and huge mouth; large hands and feet and well-developed arm and leg muscles accentuated by lack of subcutaneous fat.' The playleader was asked to take Maria 'under her wing'. When she entered the baby's cubicle Maria's face creased up behind a large dummy and she screamed until she almost turned black in the face. But each day the playleader tried and eventually she was able to pick the baby up, carry her around and take her to see the other children playing. Maria then had to be confined to bed for a 'fat balance'. The playleader visited her regularly. Maria grew to trust the playleader and a warm-hearted nurse who had taken over her regular care.

One morning Maria's face lit up and she smiled at the playleader for the first time. She began to play with large wooden beads and wooden bells, and watched, smiled and responded when the playleader spoke. The playleader recorded that her feelings towards Maria changed radically: 'The warmth of her response made me really respond to her.'

When Maria was allowed up she went to the playroom and pushed beakers around, gurgling and smiling. She played happily with a bowl of water, and sat on the floor pulling the other children's hair: 'a broad grin on her funny little face.'

Patrick (**2 years**) a spastic, was the second spastic child of Irish parents, more severely affected than his elder brother, John, who was also in hospital with him for assessment.

Patrick lay in his cot crying continuously. John was much more likeable and responsive. He was preferred by his parents who carried him around when they visited. The playleader felt that Patrick should be helped. He wailed as soon as she sat down near him. After some time she brought both brothers into the playroom and lay them on the floor. Patrick smiled, opened and closed his mouth and moved his hands slightly. The playleader tickled his tummy and rolled him gently from side to side. He gurgled and laughed and really seemed happy for the first time. 'My feelings warmed to this sad little boy when some response from him occurred. Reciprocal response seems to have been vital and I hope a valuable relationship built up.'

Children in an Eye Hospital

The eye is a precious organ and anything wrong with it becomes a focus of great anxiety. Children feel extremely worried when anything is done to their eyes, even washing them can be a nightmare to some. Many parents naturally become anxious if they suspect a visual defect.

Children who are partially sighted and those who are blind have to spend a lot of time in hospital and out-patient clinics. Squint is the commonest eye condition for which children have to attend hospital for investigation, treatment and operations—often frequent admissions.

Children with eye conditions are active and physically well when they arrive in the hospital, but as with all children, separation and adjustment to new surroundings pose many problems. The playroom and play in the ward can be reassuring; here, at least, are familiar activities of interest and fun. The playleader is there to show the new-comer what the toy cupboard contains, and how to make full use of the toys, as well as to introduce the children to each other.

Like many children with other physical handicaps, the partially-sighted child may, understandably, be over-protected. Information from the Royal National Institute for the Blind emphasizes that young children with visual defects do not receive enough extra stimulus to develop their other senses, such as hearing, touch and smell. Play in hospital shows how this can be done. These children need more companionship and warm physical contacts with other children. Sound must have meaning for them, making up for what they cannot see. If they grow up in a world of meaningless sounds—which they may well do if the radio or television is left on all day—they fail to listen effectively which can be a serious disadvantage in their education. Conversation with an interested adult helps to keep their play lively and reinforces their experiences. Play materials suitable to their stage of development must be easily available to them (Chapters 1 and 2, pp. 30–85). Shape, size and texture of these toys must be selected to give as wide a range of tactile and auditory experience as possible. The aim is to encourage the children's sense of sound and touch.

Exploring and learning to do things by themselves are important if these children are to become independent and self-supporting. The adult must learn not to interfere if there is a possibility that the child can achieve what he has set out to do. It is not easy to watch a partially-sighted child try again and again to dress a doll and repeatedly miss the right armhole or button, but unless she becomes distressed this trial and error process is how she may learn to dress the doll and herself. When the task is completed there is a rewarding sense of achievement which child and adult share.

For fear of accident, climbing, balancing and other active pursuits are often discouraged in partially-sighted children, but with play in hospital climbing apparatus has proved to be safe and popular. Parents have often watched with surprise and pleasure their children's acrobatic skills and the fun they get in spite of their impaired vision. Not only do the children enjoy this type of play but it can also demonstrate to parents what their children can do if given the opportunity. Playleaders can usefully advise on safe and stimulating play activities for home use.

A parent asked what he could provide in a small garden for his son aged 6 and partially sighted. Two strong crates, a smooth plank and a toy steering wheel firmly attached to one crate were recommended, so that car games as well as climbing, balancing and sliding would be possible. Paving stones set in the grass was another idea —to jump from one to another and to improvise a game of hop-scotch picking up objects and carrying them from one stone to the next. Giving children tools was also suggested—hammer, screw-driver, dustpan, mop—so that they could work alongside their parents and pick up new skills and interests as well as a feeling that their disability did not exclude them from everyday life.

Partially-sighted and visually handicapped children need a great deal more attention than others in all they do, otherwise they tend to relapse into apathy or boredom.

Jane, five years old and retarded, was admitted to hospital with severely impaired vision. When her grandmother visited her she was active and talkative. She knew many nursery rhymes and sang them provided she had an appreciative audience. When grandmother left she was quiet and made no effort to play with the toys on her bed. The playleader organized a group of children with paints and water play on the floor close to Jane. She sat Jane beside them and joined the group herself, encouraging Jane to splash and fill up beakers with water. Soon Jane was entertaining the group with her singing and all the youngsters joined in. After several months, Jane still needed an adult with her while she played. She learned how to do simple puzzles and played with the peg board even naming some of the colours of the pegs by holding them close to her eye and peering at them. She was inordinately proud of this success. She loved to fondle the playleader's face and hands and to have her own face gently stroked, but the moment she was left alone she gave up her attempts to play and became silent and restless. A child like Jane demands much time from the playleader, but the results are deeply rewarding as a passive child like this finds outlets in play activities for physical and mental energy within the safety limits of impaired ability.

A fretful three-year-old cheered up as soon as she found she could ride a tricycle round the ward in spite of the eye pad after a squint operation. Almost at once she seemed to play with confidence and without being worried about the cover on her eye.

Julia (**8 years**) was brought to a London hospital from the country. Her mother was pregnant and could not visit often. Her father could not leave the farm. After her operation both eyes were bandaged. The playleader spent a considerable part of the ensuing days with her. Julia liked best to dress and undress her doll which had a large wardrobe. She needed help to find the clothes and she liked to discuss what to put on next. She also needed help at mealtimes as she disliked making a mess with her food and was completely at a loss to know how to manage in her blind state. The playleader was asked by Sister to spend extra time with Julia who became very responsive to her care. The playleader was worried about leaving Julia for the weekend. She explained that she would not be able to come for the next two days but would be back on Monday. She also asked the ward auxiliary who was sympathetic with the children to spend as much time as she could with Julia and help her at mealtimes if the nurses were not available.

The playleader's work with this sensitive girl mitigated the misery she might otherwise have endured while she was in hospital.

Play gives opportunities for using judgement and making decisions which handicapped children are often denied because of the limitations of their disability. Many of these children develop special gifts and exceptional talents if they are given a chance to do so.

Suggestions for Play Activities Specially Valuable for these Children

A variety of well-made musical instruments, rattles, drums, cymbals, recorders, chimes and glockenspiel. Organized groups for music and movement, singing games, encourage a sense of rhythm and co-ordinated movement. Record players and tape recorders make a valuable contribution. Story-telling and reading aloud are part of the daily programme. 'Talking' books for older children are available with a wide range of choice in most eye hospitals.

Water play, finger painting, dough and clay, promote tactile skills and stimulating creative pursuits. Sand play cannot be ruled out, though it is prohibited in some eye hospitals. Damp sand and fine silver sand are satisfying to mould and sift.

The home corner and dressing up games provide endless outlets for the imagination and for fostering ideas of home—past, present and future. Construction toys, including model kits for cars, aeroplanes, etc., encourage thinking and manipulative skill. Blind children have been fascinated by a roll of Sellotape, which they have twisted, fingered and stuck round and over their hands and their toys. Playleaders working with 'eye patients' have noticed how the construction toy 'Playplax' with its vivid colours and smooth sides has been popular. Little ones hold the shapes to the light and peer through them while older children make elaborate colour patterns in their constructions. Climbing apparatus, trucks and tricycles provide outlets for energy and promote agility.

The Playleader and Eye Operations
The playleader dealing with 'eye patients' may have a special part to play in providing comfort and reassurance.[1]

Harry (6 years) was to have an operation for squint. When he regained consciousness he would find a pad on his eye. Sister and playleader discussed how to explain this to him. Sister told him he would have an injection which would make him feel sleepy, that he would be wheeled to the operating theatre and would be soundly asleep and feel no pain while the operation took place. When he woke up he would feel sleepy but there would also be a pad on his eye. This meant for a day or two he would not be able to use his eye but when the pad was

---

[1] G. F. Vaughan, 'Children in Hospital,' *The Lancet*, 1.1.1957.

removed he would be able to see again. The playleader took a pad from the trolley and using a teddy bear as patient showed how the pad was fixed on. Together they played with Teddy and the pad, eventually Harry put the pad over the playleader's eye and finally tried it on himself and asked for a mirror to see what he looked like.

It is unlikely that one explanation is enough. It is the repetitive play with Teddy and pad which helps the child to grasp what is going to happen. Often the child's own mother may help in preparation of this kind before he is admitted and while he is in hospital.

When he returns from the operation and is well enough, the mother or playleader can quietly talk to him reminding him of Teddy and the pad, saying that Teddy is beside him now with a pad on his eye and that later he will have his pad removed. In this way an effort has been made to manage this frightening ordeal so that the child can go through it as successfully as possible.

Severely Ill Children and Terminal Cases

As well as helping children recover from illness playleaders are faced with severely ill children for whom the prognosis is not good, and they will have to know the limitations of play in the face of advancing disease. Their warm relationship with the child and his parents can give support in the most distressing circumstances. Inner resources as well as skill are needed if compassionate help is to be given.

At one hospital the playleader wrote: 'Alice aged 10 is suffering from leukaemia and has to be alone in a cubicle. She is a wonderful child with great serenity and a beautiful mind that many people seem to have witnessed in children approaching death; she is independent and undemanding and it is easy to forget she is there. She even tried to protect her parents from knowing about her suffering. I can spend a great deal of time with her; we often have tea together which we make for ourselves in the ward kitchen. I borrow a transistor radio and we listen and discuss programmes. I used to leave her when her parents came but they often asked me to stay and they said how comforting it was just to have someone to talk to. They even wanted me there when Alice died and have written to me several times since. I felt it was the least I could do to help in this way, particularly as I had grown very fond of Alice and we enjoyed our time together.'

The Professor of Child Health wrote: 'No words can express the gratitude of Alice's parents nor the admiration of the medical and nursing staff for the professional help which the playleader gave throughout the tragic terminal illness of a deeply loved child.'

Some severely ill children are admitted frequently, receive treatment, return home and are brought back to hospital when their condition deteriorates. The playleader may work with them over a long period and share the shock of diagnosis with the parents. The parents as well as the child are helped by the knowledge that although the nursing staff may have changed, the pattern of play and playleader is still the same. A mother is comforted by seeing her child playing almost to the end supported by the same person.

The playleaders have often made contact with the social workers when they have realized that the mother has an acute need of support and has not been able to seek it out for herself.

Sonia (**4 years 6 months**) admitted with inoperable brain tumour, was unconscious for three weeks. During this time her mother rarely visited as she was too upset. Sonia regained consciousness and became interested in play. Her mother began to lose her fear of hospital and organized her home life so that she could visit every day. After five months the child was able to go home for six weeks, during this time the mother kept in touch with the playleader. During the second admission when it was clear that the child would not go home again the mother was able to discuss with the playleader the future without Sonia and the problems of the other children in the family.

The mother had short periods of depression, and the playleader made sure that the social worker visited her. The mother was reluctant to accept help as she felt the hospital was doing so much for her sick child that she could not trouble anyone with her own problems. She found it difficult to talk to people in 'white coats'. Grandmother often came to visit Sonia and all members of this closely-knit family expressed gratitude for the help they were given. Sonia was in the ward ten months before she died.

Terminal cases put immense strain on the nursing staff and on the playleader; together they do what they can to help the parents adjust to the tragic situation. If play is made as normal as possible and the parents' co-operation in caring for their child is welcomed, they can be given some consoling sense of making their own contribution to their child's last days.

Accident and Emergency Admissions

Children who are rushed into hospital as the result of an accident, or for an emergency operation, cannot be prepared in advance for the event. Sometimes they arrive in casualty departments unconscious or in a state of shock; they are nearly always confused and in pain.

It is not usually possible for the playleader to make contact with these children until after they have had surgery or treatment, but then her help can be invaluable to the child in discussing what has happened and the implications involved.

Many children in a state of 'shock' are unable to discuss

the situation. Their fears and fantasies may grow alarmingly unless someone has time and skill to sit beside them and help them sort things out. For example, **Jack (10 years)** was admitted one Friday evening and his appendix was removed that night. On Monday when the playleader arrived he was doing well but taking no interest in the ward around him and was unwilling to leave his bed. The playleader sat beside him and asked him whether he would like to paint, have a board game or join a music group in the playroom. He replied that he wanted nothing and turned his back on her. She then asked him what happened when he came into hospital but he refused to speak. The playleader told him about a boy further down the ward who had had his appendix out in the previous week. Jack turned round and stared at her. She asked him if he knew what an appendix was. He replied 'no'. The playleader told him that it was no use at all to humans but explained its use to rabbits and went on telling him that many people had their appendix out and why it sometimes gave them pain. Jack visibly relaxed, smiled and began to talk about his pain, coming to the hospital, going to the theatre, using the mask for the anaesthetic, and sharing his feelings about it all with her. He showed the playleader his wound and they talked about having the dressing changed and the stitches being taken out. Then the playleader wondered aloud about how the music group was going in the playroom and suggested going to find out. At once Jack gingerly got off his bed and staggered to the playroom, where he was soon strumming the guitar and organizing the younger children into a supporting rhythm group. His whole attitude to the operation, the people in the ward and the activities changed dramatically after the reassurance of the conversation, and his discovery that he was well enough to enjoy the music group.

In Chapter 2 (p. 72) another child was not able to discuss his accident or express his fears of the injury he had received until he painted a picture of the event. As soon as he did this he readily told the playleader and Sister of how he became involved in the car accident and how worried he felt about running across the road without looking to see what was coming.

Opportunities to help children express their fears must be carefully thought out by the playleaders, who will often observe the children and discuss the situation with Sister before making contact with the patient and deciding upon a selection of suitable play materials. Explanations must be simple, accurate and suitable for the age of the child to be beneficial, and ample opportunity must be given for children to express their feelings. Dr. Vaughan's study suggests that older children derive considerable benefit from discussion and the realization that they will be understood and cared for in an individual way while they are in hospital.

SUMMARY
by Dr. Edna Oakeshott, Lecturer, University of London Institute of Education

We cannot leave this discussion of opportunities for play for children with special problems without underlining two separate points made in the above paragraph. There is first the interprofessional relationship between the playleader and the nursing staff. A second point is the communication to the child at his own level so that there is interested concern about him as a *special* person with his own *special* problems and needs. 'Undo the gate and come and sit really close and talk to me', is only said to a favourite nurse or playleader who can be trusted to mind and understand. His knowledge of being 'me and going on being me' is enhanced by her knowledge of it.

Only when there has been communication on a private

individual basis can the child make the most fruitful use of opportunities for joint play with other children. Pulling faces at himself in a hand mirror is in line with pulling faces at your next door neighbour through the glass screen of the cubicle in an isolation ward. It is comforting that '*you* are *you* because *I* am *me*'. By such means the maintenance of identity under the most trying circumstances is ensured. Through the sharing in the provision of these opportunities between nursing and playleader staff the anxieties of caring for the ill child are pooled but not denied. Through being shared they become bearable. An extension of this interprofessional sharing is the ability developed by the hospital staff to use the skills of visiting parents. No longer is there the demand for a tidy bed but instead the provision of dough, 'Sally makes cakes for Mummy to take home each evening to cook, bringing back a more edible batch the next day for Sally and her friends to eat.' Parents of young children in hospital using opportunities such as this no longer feel redundant. Because they are able to help, their anxiety is relieved.

The everyday play of children temporarily in a hospital setting as described in Chapters 1 and 2 is now taken for granted. Provision for their needs has become almost a statutory requirement. Failure to supply this not only means grave unnecessary deprivation but also results in a consequent unruly group of unco-operative child patients demanding directly or indirectly what is rightfully theirs. But with children like those described in this chapter under the heading of special problems, the healthy open revolt is only too likely to be replaced by withdrawal into the fears and threats of lonely fantasy. And yet how easy it sounds with the playleader's skill to lure the child from his well guarded fortress.

Reading these accounts one is impressed by the ingenuity displayed not only on the practical level of the provision of play facilities but perhaps more important on the

human level in the provision of a perceiving, understanding and accepting adult. The skills and rewards of
the playleader are perhaps best identified in her own
words, 'My feelings warmed to this sad little boy when
some response from him occurred.'

4

The Role of the Hospital Playleader.
Her Work with Children and Parents

Dr. Susan Isaacs used to say, 'Play is the child's life and the means by which he comes to understand the world he lives in'. This definition lifts play right out of the category of something which merely amuses children, or helps them to pass the time.

The importance of play in a child's life with suggestions as to how it can continue and flourish in hospital has been fully discussed in preceding chapters. This chapter looks at the practical implications of the work from the playleader's point of view. There are a number of reasons why the responsibility for organizing play should rest with specially selected and trained playleaders.

At home a child's play will be encouraged mainly by his mother. Some mothers will accompany their children to hospital and a large number of hospitals in this country allow unrestricted visiting. There are many parents who do not visit for much of the time. Some children are never visited.[1]

---

[1] SURVEY carried out in 10 wards during a working week:

Wards	Monday to Friday, 9 a.m–4 p.m. Visits per day per child
1. Children's Ward, General Hospital	0·69
2. Children's Hospital: Ward 1	0·82
Ward 2	1·28
Ward 3	0·67
5. Children's Ward, Teaching Hospital	0·80
6. Children's Ward: Isolation 1	0·88
Isolation 2	0·77
8. Children's Ward, General Hospital	0·39

Even for those children who have visitors the presence of one person who has time to establish a continuous relationship on an informal basis is helpful both to children and parents. Nurses, even in those hospitals which are not short of staff, have not sufficient time nor training for what is a full-time job. Changes due to shift work and new groups of student nurses arriving every few weeks allow for no continuity or consistency of personal contact. It is important that children who are faced with a bewildering succession of medical and nursing staff should have the support of one person who comes each weekday and can spend longer periods of time with them. A rota of volunteers can be a welcome aid but should be complementary to the professional playleader and co-ordinated by her. James Robertson writes: 'Where play activities are required, it is much better that they be provided by full-time paid employees whose work relationships will have some continuity.'[1]

The playleader's main concern is with children's emotional welfare; she sees them first as children while other staff must of necessity see them as patients. In co-operation with them she is able to contribute to a more comprehensive care of the child.

The children's own interests must be the starting point for the playleader's work. She knows how to support and develop them, how to stand back and let the children make their own discoveries, and when to offer help and

| 9. Children's Ward, Teaching Hospital | 0·31 |
| 10. Children's Ward, Long Stay Hospital | 0·51 |

Weighted average for all wards surveyed, according to time of day:

Morning	0·26
Afternoon	0·50
Total	0·76

[1] *Young Children in Hospital* by James Robertson. 1970. Second edition. Tavistock Publications.

instruction so that the play is purposeful and does not end in failure and frustration. This needs experience, judgement and a sound knowledge of child development. Working in this way may look easy to the outsider, in fact it is considerably more difficult than a more formal approach, as students of education soon find out. Playleaders are concerned with children of all ages, in bed or up; in some hospitals the age-range may be 0 to 12 with occasional patients in their early teens.

The playleader moves around offering advice and encouragement, making suggestions, helping to solve problems, overcoming difficulties and taking part in discussions. Children supply the initiative once they realize the range of possible activities. Behind this turmoil of activity the playleader needs to be highly organized, for spontaneous play can only thrive if the ward, or playroom, is arranged so that patients feel free and relaxed. Small tables and chairs may be distributed round the play areas with a variety of toys and equipment attractively displayed for the children to choose from. Polythene sheets can be spread over beds, tables, chairs or floor for messy play, a home corner can be set up which can be converted into a shop or garage. If climbing boards or slides are available they must be securely fixed at a suitable height. The range of playthings will constantly be changed to stimulate new ideas and to suit the varying age groups. Paints and some form of messy play should always be available.

Play sessions can take place in the ward; the advantage of this is that children in bed, or those who are for various reasons reluctant to join in, can watch the activities and may eventually want to take part in them. The playleader can provide both for the children who are in bed, but well enough to play; and for those who are up and about, trying to keep an eye on all of them at the same time. She can also watch and see where her help is most needed. She can, for example, move over to a child whom she sees

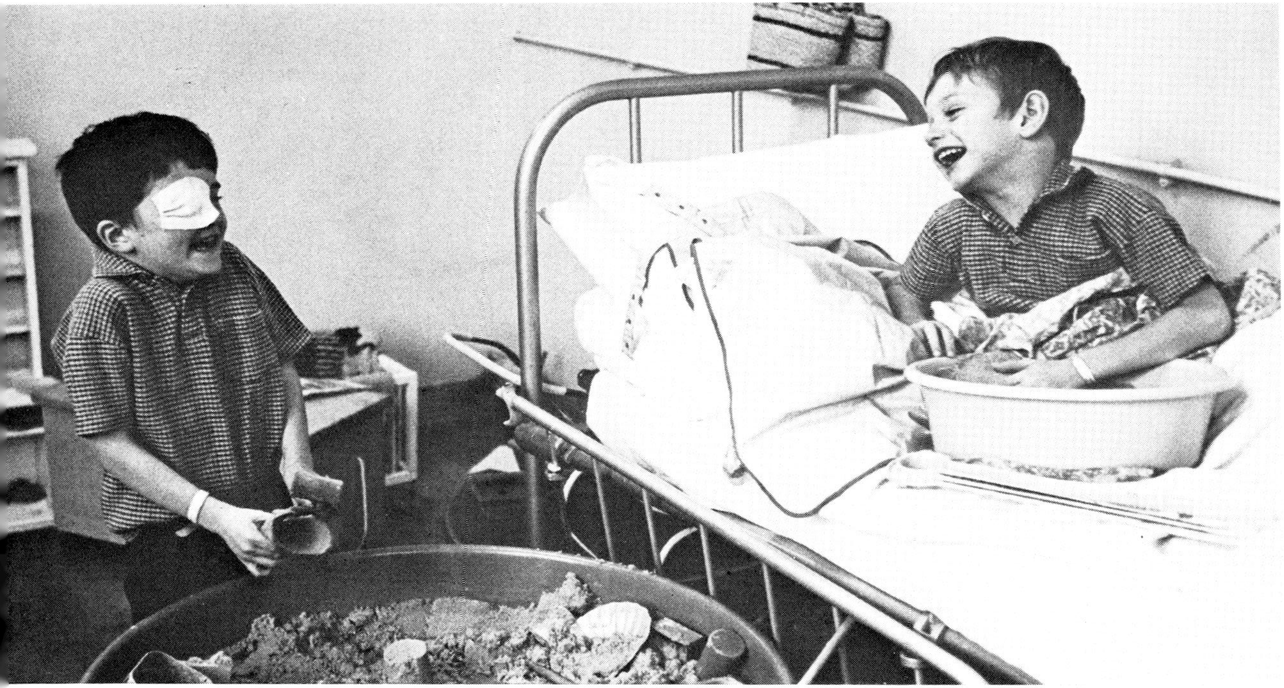

5 Useful general equipment

6 Music on the ward

absorbed in the medical examinations and treatment going on in neighbouring beds, discuss what is happening and help to allay his fears.

Alternatively, a section of the ward can be put aside as a play area. This is a successful arrangement, only if there is a glass screen so that the playleader can easily watch the children in the ward as well as those busy in the play section; there may well be some 'infiltration' with dolls' prams and tricycles. Books and toys for mobile children to take for themselves, can sometimes be displayed on a shelf or open cupboard. Children in bed will need bed-tables, trays, or specially designed easels or magnetic boards on which to play. A trolley with an assortment of equipment can be moved round the ward for patients in bed to choose from. Encouragement to play may be necessary for reluctant and shy children.

A few hospitals have separate playrooms, verandahs and outside play space. These are valuable assets, but to make full use of them it may be necessary to have two or more playleaders, nurses or parents assisting, otherwise the playleader may frequently be left alone with a group of children in the playroom so that she cannot work with those in the ward or cubicles, who are often the ones most in need of help.

Each play scheme will be different; every hospital will have a different requirement. The personalities in the ward and the aptitude of the playleader will influence the work, the architecture of the hospital and layout of the space may encourage some activities and limit others, but if there is a bed for a child there is somewhere to play and playleaders are not daunted by lack of room.

Daily Routine

On arrival each morning the playleader will probably go round the ward making an assessment for the day's work.

Sometimes there is an opportunity to discuss new patients or new problems with Sister or Staff Nurse, but the morning is a busy time for everyone and the playleader may join the nurses for Sister's report later in the day.

Then the playleader collects her equipment and sees that each child, whether flat on his back, in bed, on traction, sitting in a chair or walking about the ward chooses something to do. She looks after the youngest child, which may mean stringing a cradle toy, or a mirror, across a cot, as well as the oldest who may want to paint or play with dough. She will group the children who are up in their chairs in a corner of the ward where they can see and talk to each other and handle each other's things—in fact make real social contact. She may also group beds so that their occupants can play together and put down the sides of cots wherever possible.

Each day the work will vary according to the number of children, their ages and medical conditions. Certain children will want a great deal of individual attention. Time must be given to those in isolation cubicles, wearing gowns if necessary.

If there are a number of very young children messy activities like painting or water play will need close supervision and plans for this must be made in the daily programme. Parents, nurses and older children will often enjoy helping if they are unoccupied and the routines are explained to them. Each activity should be cleared away when it is finished and the ward tidied up in time for lunch. This can provide an opportunity for a musical session organized by older children with the younger ones joining in with rattles and drums while the playleader is putting away the toys and the tables are laid for the meal.

In the afternoon there are usually more visitors and the playleader may be free to spend time with individual children; perhaps comforting a newly admitted child who is feeling homesick and apprehensive, or taking a couple of toddlers out for a walk with a pram. She may take the opportunity to explain to a child, who is due for operation, what will happen to him, putting it all in simple terms and going over it all again with the parents when they arrive.

Between 3 and 4 o'clock the children have tea and perhaps a story before the playleader clears away toys and mess and talks about plans for the following morning.

Storage and Maintenance

Not only must clearing up be done after each session but the playleader is also responsible for storage and maintenance. Good storage space is essential; experience has shown that toys and handwork equipment used by the playleader must be locked away when she is not present as these are easily lost or mishandled in her absence. It is essential that equipment is kept in first class condition, broken and worn out materials replaced as quickly as possible. The storage cupboard should be systematically arranged so that things can be found at a moment's notice. Children's interests deteriorate into boredom and frustration unless tools and materials are readily available. Equipment is usually chosen by the play staff who have an allowance for this purpose.

Children's own possessions are kept in lockers or in sacks fixed to the side of the bed within easy reach. It is often possible to keep some toys and books in the ward to be freely distributed when play sessions are over. Very often these toys get broken and decrepit unless the playleader discards and renews them at her discretion.

Continuity

Playleaders usually work a five day week from 9 a.m. to 4 p.m. with an hour off for lunch. Children would benefit from an extension of these hours to cover the early evening and the weekends. Most playleaders have one month's annual leave and whenever possible this is not taken when the hospital school teachers are away so that play is available for most of the year.

The playleader can prepare each child for her next visit and for the times when she is unable to come at weekends or during her holidays. Since being in hospital gives rise to considerable feelings of insecurity it is important that the playleader should make it clear to the children that she will come back. For older children the time or day can be specified and plans made for the next session. The playleader should convey a sense of her continuing interest and the durability of the relationship she has made. Without such assurance some children may be quite unable to play on their own, the moment they are left their activity dwindles. **Jane (3 years)** had been given a painting book and coloured pencil but showed no interest in them except during the few minutes a nursery nurse could spare time to talk to her. She spent the rest of the time head-rolling —a symptom of distress.

Detailed observations were made, comparing the length of time for which children persisted with play when well provided with opportunities, with periods when no supervised provision was made.[1] In wards with supervised play the children settled with their occupations for an average of 39·4 minutes. In wards with no playleader the average length of settled play was 3·8 minutes. That is to say, children well provided with play opportunities played with absorption for periods ten times as long as those without such provision.

Behaviour Problems

Providing a good context for play is not something which can be done incidentally in the general round of ward

---

[1] *Play and the Sick Child.* Eva Noble. Faber & Faber, 1967.

duties. The playleader needs time to attend to the children individually, as well as the specialized training to recognize problems and deal with them as they arise.

Wendy (**3 years 10 months**) had a dislocated hip and bore signs of bodily ill-treatment when she came in. She screamed loudly whenever anyone tried to wash her. She was given soap and water to play with. At the time of observation she had calmed down and was happily bathing a doll and washing its hair. While this was going on she allowed herself to be washed.

Suitable play activities are not only beneficial in themselves but have the added bonus of being an easy means of communication between adults and children and between children themselves. As a result, relationships are made in the most natural way. Situations can be created where friendships are likely to arise by bringing mobile children to play with those in bed; sometimes two bed-bound children can be placed on opposite ends of a large bed or a group can be gathered round a bed for a story with discussion afterwards. Once it is understood how children can be helped to support each other, ingenious ways will be found to bring them together.

The reaction of some children to stress is to withdraw from contact with the outside world. Because their behaviour makes little or no demands on busy ward staff such children may be overlooked. The playleader, as a trained observer with time to break through such defences, is able to see that these children, who may be the ones most in need of help, get it.

Sandra (**1 year 8 months**) spent an hour of observation time quietly staring into space virtually ignored. She was alone in a bare cubicle with no toys and the door shut. Such was her intense inner confusion beneath her exterior silence that when at last someone went to give her a little of the attention she so urgently needed she burst into tears. Children undergoing such terrible inner stress need skilled help and understanding, and it is with such withdrawn children that skilled playleadership can achieve remarkable results.

Janet (**6 years 4 months**) admitted with a kidney disease, was dangerously ill and did not respond to anyone. For nearly three months she remained completely 'mute'. Day after day, week after week, the playleader went and talked to her although the child made no response. The playleader knew exactly what she was doing and one day Janet asked her to sit and draw for her. The playleader talked about a journey she had made into the country, sketching as she talked. Janet became deeply absorbed asking for more details and explanations From then on she began to take an interest in all that went on around her. With so serious a case of withdrawal the playleader was prepared for the relapse which came but was soon overcome. Janet's physical condition began to improve so that she could take an increasing part in the play activities of the ward. Her chances of recovery had been considered very poor, but her improvement was so great that when she left hospital she was able to attend a Special School.

The management of children with aggressive and destructive behaviour also needs skill. The playleader must judge how far the destruction can be allowed to go and provide a framework of security in which the child can legitimately express his hostile feelings. Sometimes she will join in these activities and provide play material to match up with the situation.

Owen (**4 years**) seemed only interested in disrupting other children's play. He went from child to child sweeping puzzles, paint, beads, etc., on to the floor, upsetting children and pursuits with a reckless abandon. The playleader had to restore order without losing friendly contact with Owen or the group. As soon as settled play returned she took Owen to one corner and fetched a sack of large bricks; they sat down together building and knocking down towers and were joined by other children. Owen was the centre of the group, and he and the playleader talked as they played. The game fascinated him and the playleader decided to have regular sessions of play with him using bricks, clay, hammer and nails, drum and drumsticks.

Tommy (**6 years**) broke the glass window in his cubicle, pulled the electric flex from the wall and was a real menace to the medical and nursing staff. Fortunately he was well enough to be able to go outside. The playleader spent some hours each day with him in the hospital grounds where he climbed trees, kicked a football and ran races with another boy. On his return to the ward he behaved in a more controlled and less destructive way.

It is never easy in any group when children are hostile to each other; some bite, hit and scratch. It is essential to comfort the injured and maintain friendly relations with the attacker while at the same time expressing disapproval of his actions. It does not help an angry child to be allowed to break up toys as too much guilt is attached to this behaviour for it to be therapeutic. This is where unstructured play materials are invaluable. Adults vary in the amount of destructive play they themselves can tolerate without losing sympathy with the child—toleration can be increased by training and experience, coupled with an awareness of the aggressive child's problems and of one's own particular response to destructive behaviour.

Extensions of a Playleader's Role

So far this chapter has described the playleader's basic operational tasks in organizing and developing play in the wards. But further demands have been made upon her as the work has progressed, extending the scope of her responsibilities. These extensions were not totally unexpected, but their importance turned out to be much greater than anticipated. Some of these demands have been made by the children and their parents, others by the medical and nursing staff. Effective response depends on the playleader's awareness of these demands, and being prepared to deal with them.

In 1963 the first Save the Children Fund hospital playgroup was started at the Brook Hospital, Woolwich. It was obvious after only a few months that the presence of a playleader in the ward was giving children and parents comfort and reassurance, as has happened in all subsequent SCF hospital playgroups. The intensity with which the younger children deprived of their parents demanded 'mothering' from the playleader was even greater than expected.

In hospital the playleader may be the one to supplement a mother's care when she cannot be there, showing qualities which children value in their own parents, particularly by being the person who will see them through their ordeals. To do this well the playleader must have sympathy for the parents as well as the children. Substitution for a mother's warm physical affection is an urgent need of sick children, particularly the younger ones. Many children will spontaneously seek the comfort of close contact with playleaders, others will respond with alacrity when it is offered.

As part of such substitute-mothering playleaders may assist with dressing children, taking them to the lavatory, washing them and helping with meals. For some patients meal-times are the big events of the day. Playleaders can help the nursing staff with feeding children—seeing that the right-sized cutlery and helpings are given, making sure that children are not sat down at the table long before the food arrives so that when it comes they are fractious and cannot enjoy the meal. They can help to make meals a social occasion rather than a routine procedure.

Before taking children to the lavatory the playleader must find out if specimens are being collected and she must ask help from the nursing staff if necessary.

Playleaders use their judgement in standing in for mothers, sometimes reminding children old enough to understand that they do this in a temporary capacity. Nurses should not assume that playleaders will always undertake these duties. On no account should the playleader be used as an excuse for excluding mothers. Often playleaders have suggested that parents be urged to visit more frequently as they have noticed how severely disturbed some of the children were by the separation. This was particularly noticeable on one occasion when the playleader had a number of very young children in the playroom—too many for her to mother, yet all anxiously demanding the individual attention which she could not give.

Older children will often use the playleader as a friend or confidante, discussing their problems and asking for explanations about treatment or the condition of other patients. Direct and truthful answers must be given whenever possible and if promises are made they must be kept. Many questions concerning their illnesses will be referred to doctors and nurses, and ways of handling these will be discussed with the ward team. As she gains experience she will learn more difficult techniques, such as how to encourage children to discuss things which she and the children find painful; and how to curb too hasty reassurance or sympathy which may prevent a child from communicating what he feels.

Playleader and Parents

An important feature of the playleader's work is in getting to know the child's parents or frequent visitor. She will be able to find out many details of the child's home routine, his likes and dislikes and the things he most fears. She will also discover how much or how little he has been prepared for his visit to hospital. By doing this she will be seen by the child as joining in his experience.

Leaving a small child for the first time in a hospital ward can be an agonizing experience for parents and child. If the playleader can do something to comfort the child at the moment of separation the pain for all can be much relieved. From this moment parents may feel they have a friend in the ward to turn to in moments of stress.

This kind of sympathetic help from the playleader will encourage parents to work with her to the benefit of their child. Initially some parents may resent the presence of a playleader and feel themselves supplanted by her. The more parents tell the playleader about their child the easier it will be for her to keep the image of home and family alive in his mind between their visits. For example, friendly chat with one grandmother gave the playleader a picture of a three-year-old patient's home in the country. She could use this mental picture in talking to him when he had no visitors. In the same way if snapshots of parents and family, home and garden, pets or favourite toys are on his locker they can be used as a starting point of conversation.

When parents visit their child for the first time in hospital they may find it difficult to make contact with him. Because he has missed them so much he may be unwilling to respond to their friendly overtures. The playleader can sometimes explain to parents the reasons for their child's reactions; why he seems so disinterested when they arrive and screams when they leave. She can explain the importance of telling him the truth and of saying, for instance, that they will come back tomorrow only if they are certain that they can do this. She can encourage them to say 'good-bye' firmly and calmly and not just slip away hoping to 'spare his feelings'. She can suggest that the mother leaves her handkerchief, glove or empty purse for the child to look after for her as a tangible sign that she will return.

Once children have settled into hospital they may prefer to continue with a playgroup activity even while their parents are visiting. It is important that the playleader makes sure that parents feel welcome in the ward or playroom at all times. With unrestricted visiting parents are liable to arrive at any time during the day so the playleader has to be flexible in organizing her work.

Some mothers with no first-hand knowledge of nursery school activities may be surprised, even shocked, at what the children are allowed to do with sand, water, clay and paint. Some may feel that this kind of play is unhygienic in hospital. But many, having seen the playleader organize messy materials successfully, and the children thoroughly engrossed in the occupations, may be encouraged to introduce some of them later on at home.

Parents have many anxieties about their children in hospital.[1] Often they do not know when, or whom, to ask about their child's progress, day of release, etc. In their anxiety they may question people on the ward who are unable to help them, such as student nurses or ward cleaners, partly because these people are more approachable than senior staff. If, for the same reasons, they ask the playleader things about their child that she is unable to answer, she should advise them to talk to the sister or house physician. The playleader may also have to deal tactfully with parents who, out of anxiety, or curiosity, ask questions about the illness and treatment of other children.

Time and again the playleader is called upon to be a patient listener. It is of immense help to parents to have

---

[1] 'The Captive Mother.' S. R. Meadows. *Archives of Disease in Childhood,* Vol. 44, No. 235, 1969. Also reprinted in *New Society,* 21.8.69. 14.360.287.

someone they can talk to about their child's welfare, their home circumstances or their own feelings. The playleader acts as a safety valve for all parents but especially for those whose children are on the danger list.

Despite the widespread publicity given in recent years to the importance of visiting children in hospital many parents do not make as much use of unrestricted visiting as they could, and, in fact, visit their sick children infrequently or not at all, because they do not consider it necessary or desirable. Having handed their child over to the hospital they feel that it is probably best not to interfere. They hate to see their child cry at visiting times so they keep away altogether. The playleader can help such parents by explaining that it is quite natural for their child to be upset and to cry but that this is much better for him than bottling up his feelings of fear, loneliness and resentment, which is what will happen if they do not visit and he feels abandoned by them. It has to be remembered that many parents can only visit in the evenings because they both work all day. Others have home commitments and cannot spend long in the ward.

Many children from overseas may not have visitors. It is important to help them keep in touch with home by letters, pictures and magazines. If approached the British Red Cross or Embassy Staff will endeavour to find a visitor who can speak the appropriate language.

The playleader can help parents with some of the problems when their child comes home. The useful leaflet *Coming into Hospital* prepared by the National Association for the Welfare of Children in Hospital has this to say: 'Young children may be unsettled and rather difficult to manage for a while after a stay in hospital and this is more likely when their parents have been unable to visit regularly. Disturbed behaviour may last several weeks and a great deal of sympathy and understanding will be needed. Even though your child may seem to turn against you, try to be patient and give the extra love and reassurance that he needs at this time, until his sense of security is recovered. Never threaten to send a child back to hospital as a punishment.'

There is some evidence to show that mothers living in hospital need to be helped to find their place in the life of the ward.[1] If they receive no guidance from the staff about what they may or may not do for their children they may well become bewildered and bored by life in hospital. Where there is a well-run playgroup in the ward mothers may, at first, feel they have even less to do for their children than when there is no hospital playleader or organized play facilities. It is therefore up to the playleader and nursing staff to explain to these mothers what they can do for their own children and how they can help children who have not got living-in mothers or visitors. Once well settled in the ward a resident mother may be able to look after a small group of children while the playleader attends to others, make and mend equipment or do other tasks which appeal to her.

Sometimes a child may be reluctant to join in a group activity; he may, for example, prefer to sit on his mother's knee rather than do finger painting with the others. As play is organized solely for the children's benefit the playleader will not urge him to join in. Often sick children fasten intensely upon their mothers and cannot tolerate her helping with others in the ward.

Playleaders as Observers

In many hospitals playleaders will be asked by the staff to give informal accounts of specific children's behaviour. They are in an ideal position to make observations on a

---

[1] Hospital Admission Leaflet. Obtainable from the National Association for the Welfare of Children in Hospital, 74 Denison House, 296 Vauxhall Bridge Road, London, S.W.1.

child at play and on his relationships with parents, staff and other children. Observations they make can lead to further investigations of a more formal kind.

If the qualified playleader has had previous experience with healthy children, and especially training in child development, she will be able to make useful contributions to the discussions between professional staff on the ward. Her observations are more valid if she knows a few simple facts about the children's illnesses and home backgrounds. Some playleaders attend a daily briefing session with the nurses; others are given information about the patients by the sister on arrival each day; some have access to the patients' notes.

At the Brook Hospital, Woolwich, the playleader records observations which are included in some patients' notes. The SCF playleaders report on their work every four months. Their reports are presented to the doctors concerned, the playgroup supervisors and the professional committee at SCF headquarters which is responsible for the policy of this work.

In some hospitals there are weekly meetings for professional staff working in the children's wards where cases are discussed from medical, nursing and welfare viewpoints. Playleaders learn a great deal from these meetings and contribute their observations which are often used in influencing the treatment of the child. In this way the playleader becomes a real member of the paediatric team.

Mandy (11 years) was suffering from a metabolic disorder. A psychiatrist asked three nurses and the playleader to fill in a detailed questionnaire daily on the behaviour of this patient. The doctors were trying to balance the most appropriate diet for her condition and needed impartial observation on any changes in her behaviour. The observations were valuable and playleaders are now being used more often in this way.

Support during Treatment

Many playleaders help nursing staff by holding children during treatment, when such things as injections or eye drops are given or stitches removed. Often the nurse will join in the play which helps to integrate treatment with all that goes on in the ward. Sometimes playleaders escort children to the plaster room, X-ray departments or to the operating theatre. The decision on who accompanies the child rests with Sister. The playleader is frequently asked by the patients to explain the reason for treatment and medical procedures. This she does as accurately as possible so that children understand what is happening to them.

At Fulham Hospital under the guidance of Dr. Hugh Jolly and the Ward Sisters, the play specialists (as they are called here), are expected to explain medical and surgical procedures in detail to the children—if possible the parents are involved as well. Play materials and dolls may be used with masks, hypodermic syringes, stethoscopes, etc., to demonstrate techniques—play specialists, parents and patients all play and practise with the apparatus. This work is quite distinct from the children's spontaneous play with doctors' and nurses' kits which they use whenever they like in the play areas.

Derek (4 years) was admitted for chest trouble and a series of tests had to be done over a period of four days. This was explained to Derek and he was told his stomach had to be emptied each morning before breakfast. Sister gave the play specialist all the different things she would use. The play specialist showed them to Derek and explained how and why Sister would use them. While she was explaining, Derek's mother arrived and he told her exactly what was going to happen to him, his mother was very interested and pleased that he was being prepared in this way. Later in the day the play specialist gave Derek and his mother a teddy bear and they played the whole thing through again. Next morning Derek told the play specialist what had happened and again used Teddy as the patient. Not all parents are able to co-operate in treatment as fully as Derek's mother did.

Staff Selection and Administration

Descriptions of the qualities and accomplishments required for some jobs tend to sound like a catalogue of all the virtues; the one for a playleader is no exception. The training of a hospital playleader has to be wide and varied, based on the principles of normal child development and the purposes of play, but flexible enough to foster all possible opportunities for natural development in the unnatural hospital setting. She has to understand the children's language of play and respond to it in countless unpredictable ways. The demands on the playleader are enormous but the work is fascinating and never monotonous or repetitive.

The satisfaction gained from this work is very different from that of caring for children in residential homes, day nurseries, or schools, where relationships are built up over a period of time, and a contribution is made to long-term development. In hospital the aim is to support the child through a crisis and to handle the experience as humanely as possible. The results of this support are not always apparent but when they are it is rewarding for the staff.

During the first three months after opening the playgroup at Brook Hospital (1963) sixty children aged 15 months to 12 years took part in play activities. One for the whole period, two for about six weeks, some for two or three weeks, and some for only a few days. The playleader had to deal with this ever-changing population and adapt quickly to every child's needs.

It should also be borne in mind that the playleader has

7 The doctor asked the playleader to encourage activities to exercise the undamaged eye

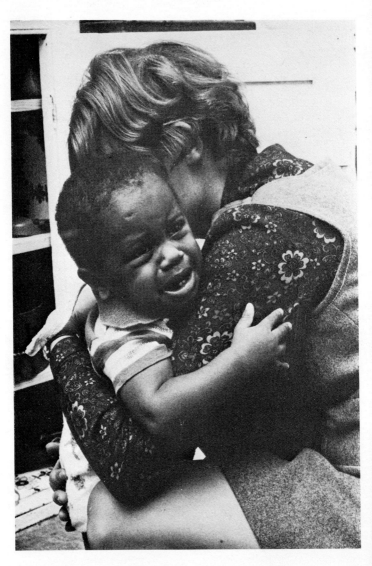

8   A new friend in hospital

to co-operate with changing staff on the wards. Their training and experience will usually be very different from hers so that she is in the unenviable position of working in full view of other staff who may not understand either her techniques or her objectives. However, there is a positive side to this situation since it offers opportunities to explain briefly to large numbers of students what playleaders are doing. Some playleaders have been asked to give regular talks about their work to medical students and student nurses. One hospital management committee sends pupil nurses to observe the work of the hospital playleader.

The SCF pilot scheme for play in hospital started in 1963, has expanded because doctors and senior nursing staff have asked for this service. In 1970 there were 18 hospital play schemes in London and the provinces and large numbers of requests had to be refused through lack of funds. It therefore seems appropriate to describe in some detail how SCF playleaders are chosen and the groups administered.

Playleaders are selected as much for their personal attributes and experience as for their training; nursery and primary school teachers, nursery nurses (NNEB) are all suitable candidates. Mature nursery nurses who have been given extra training can be extremely good as they have often specialized in the care of babies and toddlers whereas many teachers have not had this experience. Teachers and nursery nurses working together with their own special contributions can make an excellent team. It is not advisable for a playleader to work with more than 15 children at once. The SCF playgroup committee feels that the playleader's work which is both educational and therapeutic should be firmly linked to the local education authority. Interdepartmental discussion between health and education representatives would be valuable.

All the SCF work is supervised by an experienced

145

teacher who has made a special study of children in hospital. She takes part in the selection and appointment of staff in co-operation with the hospital concerned. Great importance is attached to the regular visits which the supervisor makes to each hospital playgroup, the advice she gives and the co-ordination of playgroup work which she achieves. The playleader's experiences are shared and individual problems dealt with at source. The supervisor arranges frequent meetings and visits of special interest. She acts as a clearing house for information about equipment which has proved useful for different kinds of handicap or disability. There is also a seminar with a paediatrician for all the staff in the London area. Here the staff discuss their problems and their feelings about the work they are doing. In this way they learn from each other as well as from the paediatrician. These meetings help to support them in their work and increase their insight and therapeutic skills.

In the future supervisors might be based at various hospitals and be involved in the practical work of the play schemes there. The number of supervisors needed will have to be considered in relation to the number of wards with playgroups and the type of work the playleaders are doing. SCF staff working in hospital have the advantage of belonging to a department which has long experience of running playgroups in a variety of situations and opportunities for meeting colleagues engaged in work similar to their own.

It has been suggested that it is not advisable to introduce yet another professional worker into the group of devoted specialists already working as a ward team. In recognizing the importance of play for the health of the child the nurse's role must not be impoverished by making it appear as if she and the doctors do all the unpleasant tasks for the children while the playleaders do the pleasant ones. However, it is important in the development of children that they should learn to integrate their good and bad experiences with the same person and make total relationships on that basis with both nurse and playleader. In most hospitals with SCF play schemes where nurses join in play and playleaders are present during treatment, such integration happens naturally.

At present nurses are scarce and often overworked so it would be difficult to impose on them yet another branch of training and a new and additional responsibility to organize play facilities, but in the future this could happen.

Where the work of the playleader is undertaken by parents and voluntary helpers some benefit is apparent, but the full value of play to disturbed and sick children cannot be achieved. Successful play schemes have evolved where professional playleaders have organized and worked closely with voluntary workers.

In addition to the SCF hospital playleaders there are a growing number of trained, professional playleaders running individual hospital playgroups in various parts of the United Kingdom.

Going to hospital may be the first major crisis in a child's life. If all concerned—parents, hospital and play staff—support the child through this experience with sympathy and understanding, he will be strengthened to face future ordeals with less apprehension and fear.

5

Working with others on the Ward

A hospital ward like any unit in which a number of people work together is a web of relationships. In this network the playleader occupies a special but isolated position, midway, as it were, between the doctors, nurses and other hospital personnel on the one hand, and the lay people on the other—the patients, their relations and, perhaps, volunteers. The full development of her role depends largely on the quality of her relationships with the other people in the ward. It is a fact that she spends a great deal of her time, talking, explaining, reassuring and listening. As one experienced leader said: 'One does so much more than play with the children.'

Paediatrician and Playleader

The playleader from the paediatrician's point of view has three main functions: (1) she provides play, (2) she acts as a parent substitute, (3) she is a new source of information.

(1) The playleader acts as a bridge between life at home and life in hospital. She will encourage the child to do in the ward many of the things he did at home. If his activities are likely to be restricted in any way after leaving hospital she can help to prepare him for the change. Absence of this service may be as damaging psychologically to him as his illness. By ensuring his enjoyment of interesting activity and by stimulating his curiosity and exploration she is contributing towards his recovery.

(2) As a parent substitute she is virtually the only adult in hospital with whom the child comes into contact who

will never be part of the procedures necessary for his treatment. She will give him close physical comfort, talk with him and support him through the ordeal of bodily interference, whether he is being put into plaster, or having a lumbar puncture; she is his ally. She may help him to know and understand what is happening, and even express for him what he may be feeling.

(3) By her special contact with the child she may, to some extent, be able to provide the doctors and nurses with valuable information about him for instance by observing his reactions; his withdrawal, or his responsiveness to a particular activity. He will, through play and conversation, be demonstrating something of what he is feeling and experiencing. The playleader by her observations of his behaviour will be a useful source of information which might otherwise not be available.

The Playleader and the Ward Sister

Subject to the broad principles of treatment laid down by the doctors, the ward sister carries the whole responsibility for the care of the children in her ward; everyone else there works under her guidance and instruction. If she and the playleader get on well together there is almost no limit to the range of questions they can discuss including when and how to prepare children for treatment and surgery, who is to do this, who goes with them to treatment room or X-ray unit or to the operating theatre. It is the sister's attitude to play which determines whether it succeeds or fails in her ward. If she understands the purposes of play in a hospital setting she will encourage it and explain it in such a way to the doctors, nurses, students, parents, cleaners and others, that it cannot fail to be a success. If, however, she is doubtful about its real value and mistrusts the playleader it will never really catch on.

When playleaders are appointed to a hospital under the

SCF scheme the sister is always present on the selection committee with the paediatrician and the matron to decide which candidate shall be chosen. In this way she can help to choose someone whom she feels will fit in with her own requirements on the ward.

In good circumstances the sister and playleader work out together which children are to be included in the daily play programme—sister may ask for certain children to be given special attention. Sometimes it is necessary to encourage a child who is in the post-operative stage to become active. The sister can explain the effect of drugs on the behaviour of children so that the playleader will know what to expect and will not feel discouraged by lack of response. She can usefully instruct the playleader about the different illnesses in the ward and how these modify a child's capacity to play. She will sometimes ask for special activities for a child who has not used a limb because it has been in plaster and the playleader may need to devise play to stimulate mobility.

Each ward has its own normal rules and daily routine. This framework is useful but there are times when rules can be broken, for example, children not allowed to eat before operations can be allowed to continue playing while the others clear up their games and prepare for a meal. At times the playleader must be prepared to justify the arrangements she has made for play.

The playleader learns from the sister how to react to emergencies. A blood transfusion may have to be given to a child and a group of children moved away to continue their activities with as little upheaval as possible. Sometimes a child in the playroom may have a fit and the playleader must know the procedure for that child and the others in her care. When the ward is full, when children are seriously ill, when staff are short, tension will mount. At such times sister and the nurses may find the clutter of playthings more than they can stand. The playleader must be aware of these occasions and plan accordingly for quieter activities. By using her common sense in this way the playleader can prevent relationships between herself and the nursing staff becoming strained. Most playleaders are ready to help in any way they can in an emergency, undertaking, perhaps, to feed or bath a child if no nurse is available.

Friendships are fostered between play and nursing staff if the sister encourages her nurses to play with their patients when they are free from other duties. In this way the nurses learn a great deal about the children, they enjoy the play and the children certainly do. Sadly in some hospitals it is the Matron who disapproves of nurses playing with the patients. There you may see nurses doing trivial things while the playleader is struggling single-handed with a large number of children of mixed ages and would obviously welcome help.

Some sisters have said that before the playleader was appointed they often had a nagging feeling that the children were bored, boisterous or listless through lack of attention which neither they nor the nursing staff were able to give. A number of sisters who were questioned by representatives of the Department of Health and Social Security said that they would prefer *not* to be responsible for running their own play schemes as they did not feel sufficiently qualified to do this nor would they welcome a fresh responsibility.

In the SCF scheme the Group Supervisor is always available to talk to the sister and play staff. Having a third party outside the ward like this is an advantage. Sister can discuss questions with her concerning play and the play-leaders, and the supervisor can advise on the introduction of activities.

Playleader and the Nurses

A good relationship between the playleaders and nurses

makes a great contribution to the happiness of the ward. This means asking each other's advice, giving and asking for help and, above all, realizing that everyone tries to do their best for the children often under testing conditions. Mature people will understand that in this situation jealousy can easily arise and that it is essential to talk things through before matters get out of hand.

Playleaders can learn from an experienced nurse such things as: ways of making children comfortable, ways of lifting them, giving them drinks, explaining treatments to them, also how to deal with vomiting, defaecating, etc. Reciprocally, playleaders often help nurses by holding children for treatment or by discussion, help the less experienced with their anxieties in handling sick children. A young nurse, for example, may feel incompetent when her ministrations to a small child, perhaps undressing and bathing him, evoke tears. 'Unrealistically she thinks that a more skilled person could do the task without upsetting the child. She may not know that the response she is getting is inevitable and inherent in the situation.'[1] The danger is that she may protect herself against the impact of the child's tears and her own feelings of inadequacy and humiliation by adopting an attitude of insensitivity.

Very often young nurses first coming on to a children's ward are eager to play naturally and spontaneously with the children. Then they begin to feel that this is not 'professional' behaviour and they withdraw and cut themselves off from the children. They may also be afraid of becoming too intimately involved with the children and vulnerable to their suffering.[2] The presence of a playleader can help to confirm a young nurse's belief in the rightness of her natural instinct to behave warmly towards the children, so she will not repress her feelings and the children will benefit.

---

[1] *Children under Stress.* By Sula Wolff. Allen Lane, The Penguin Press, 1969.
[2] *Ibid.*

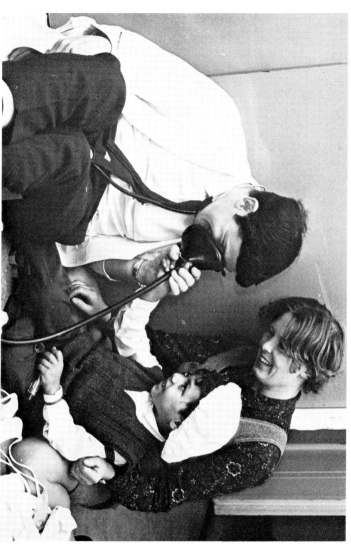

9 Preparation for surgery. The doctor is anaesthetised

11 Playleader and
nurse work together

10 Mother, nurse
and playleader

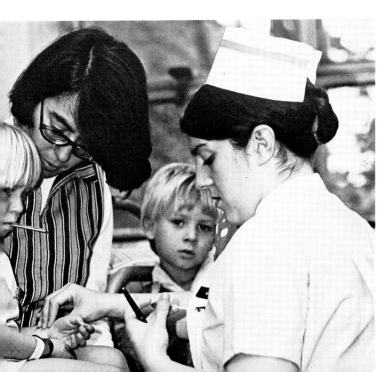

12 Showing off the scar

Nurses can learn a lot from watching how playleaders work with children and they often adopt the same techniques. Many pupil nurses who come into children's wards do so as part of their general training, and some have no interest in nursing children—nor aptitude. Some are quite unaware that children need to be handled differently from adult patients. If the sister is backed up by the play staff in the way the children are cared for, the nurses benefit by seeing consistent methods being used, and sister has an ally in her arduous task of demonstrating paediatric nursing techniques to successive groups of students.

A few hospitals second their student nurses to work as helpers under a playleader for a few weeks as part of their training. One training hospital sends pupil nurses to visit play schemes in other hospitals and they are given the opportunity to discuss their observations with the playleader. This can give future nurses real insight into the value of play. Other hospitals send student nurses out into nursery schools to observe healthy children. In one hospital the playleader gives regular talks to the pupil nurses on her function in the ward, explaining the value of play for health and development. It is to be hoped that all these training methods will be much more widely used in the future.

Several doctors have said that the presence of play staff in the ward over a period of time has enabled all concerned to grow in sympathy and understanding for children under stress.

The Playleader and Hospital School Teachers

Most children in hospital have neither playleader nor teacher (1971). A few children's wards have both. Where this happens it is important that each of them should fully understand what the other is doing and show mutual respect for each other's work. They should be seen to co-operate so that there is a feeling of everyone working together for the good of each child. There may be difficulties when some children are playing while others are expected to work but this is when conviction of the worthwhileness of both jobs will help in putting across the reasons to the children. Any hint of antagonism will encourage the children to try playing one off against the other. If lessons are fun and exciting, as they should be, and play is experience of learning, as it should be, then both playleader and teacher are working together to the same end. Both are concerned that the child should develop in a normal harmonious way.

It has been said that: 'The basis for good work in the education and welfare of children in hospital is patience, tolerance and understanding of each other's role.'[1] Difficulties occur through lack of communication. There should be opportunities for informal contact between teachers, playleaders and other hospital staff so that they can discuss their respective jobs—what they are doing and why. In practical terms this may mean providing facilities so that they can have their mid-morning break and meals together. Playleader and teacher share information about the children's individual needs and problems. Case conferences with medical and nursing staff besides being of benefit to the children, are an effective means of apprising members of a ward team of each other's work and contribution. The work of both teacher and playleader is more effective in wards where it is actively appreciated rather than just 'accepted' by other ward staff.

Teachers and playleaders working in small units often experience a professional isolation that makes it difficult

---

[1] *Children in Hospital.* Papers given at the Association for Special Education Conference, Liverpool, 1965. Available from: S. Hamer, A.S.E. Branch Secretary, Royal Liverpool Children's Hospital School, Heswall, Cheshire. 17½p.

for them to keep in touch with modern educational and child development studies. They both need regular contact with others working in their fields—teachers with other teachers and the officers of the local education authority; playleaders with others working in primary and nursery education and those organizing hospital and community playgroups.

Because teachers and playleaders work closely together in some hospitals it is worth having a brief look at the work of the hospital teacher. It must be realized that school and teachers are immensely significant to school-age children who spend about 1,400 hours in school every year. Even if a child dislikes school he recognizes teachers as important people who spell everyday routine by their presence. As children stay for shorter periods in hospital the role of the teacher is changing. No longer is the main emphasis on preventing the children from falling behind in their school work, but rather in helping them to meet and integrate this disturbing experience.

The teacher who sees her role as therapeutic as well as instructive realizes that she herself and what she has to offer spells the normal and familiar to children in a situation where fear may loom large. Such a teacher is aware of 'children's interests and curiosities, of how to feed and stimulate their minds';[1] she will be ready to listen and to talk through problems that the children's illnesses create for them, and then provide lively, interesting activities to give them positive goals. All this is quite consistent with providing formal teaching for the individual child who may be worried that he is dropping behind his class mates, especially if examinations are imminent.

It is difficult for a single teacher to provide adequate teaching in all subjects for secondary school children and often it is desirable to enlist the help of specialist tutors.

[1] *Ibid.*

The teacher has to be prepared to write to or to visit the child's own school, collect textbooks, curriculum, perhaps even arrange for work to be collected from hospital and corrected at school and for his school teacher to visit him in hospital. At one North London Hospital School the headmistress is so closely in touch with her area schools that she knows which textbooks the children use in each class! At another hospital the teacher visits the local school in order to assess what the older sick children will be missing and how she can fill the gaps. Some hospital teachers feel that there are very good opportunities for giving remedial teaching in hospital which are not always exploited as much as they could be. Three or four weeks of continuous, skilled teaching can help a backward reader enormously. Such opportunities do not always occur in the normal school setting.

Overlapping Roles

Before playleaders were appointed to hospitals, teachers were often hampered in their work with older children by the vociferous demands of the under-fives. When a ward has the services of both a teacher and a playleader the latter will usually be responsible for the younger children leaving the teacher free to concentrate on the older ones. Some teachers only work with individual children, others will have group teaching sessions depending on the ages of the children at any one time in the ward. Where no one has been appointed to organize the pre-school children a teacher may well provide play materials for the little ones and generally include them in her group. Available evidence, which is very limited, seems to show that teachers are running a number of hospital playgroups.[1]

---

[1] In a recent analysis of play facilities in 74 hospitals the National Association for the Welfare of Children in Hospital found:

28 organized by a teacher on her own   2 by occupational therapists
12 organized by a teacher with helpers   2 by volunteers

Teachers for long-stay Children

Long-stay children are dealt with in detail in Chapter 3, pp. 93–100. Hospital school teachers only work in school terms but some hospital schools now stagger their holidays. Some children feel it is really outrageous to be admitted to hospital in the holidays and then have to *do lessons as well!* In these circumstances many teachers will provide activities rather than formal lessons. It is a great help if the teachers and playleaders can plan their holidays so that children in hospital are 'covered' for most of the year. In some hospitals the teachers cover the year assisted by play-centre staff during vacations. The Inner London Education Authority (I.L.E.A.) has provided play-centre staff for the holidays in at least one hospital. At the Royal National Orthopaedic Hospital, Stanmore, the children are occupied during school holidays by a paid staff of play-leaders recruited from Colleges of Education and supervised by members of the teaching staff. 'Holidays' mean nothing to children in hospital unless this sort of provision is made.

Summary

There is no real dichotomy between play and education, between the role of the playleader and the role of the teacher. Where a hospital school already exists it would seem reasonable to extend this to include playgroups rather than to introduce a new service, providing the excellent relationships with medical and nursing staff are maintained.

---

12 by voluntary playleaders
9 by professional playleaders
3 by cadet nurses
3 by nursery nurses

1 by a nurse
1 by a recreation officer
1 by pre-nursing students

The Playleader and the Physiotherapist

Playleaders have frequently co-operated with physio-therapists to continue some aspects of treatment in the play sessions—in many cases this has been highly successful.

Joe (**1 year, 10 months**) was the youngest child of a family of seven, living in cramped, squalid housing. He was underweight, quiet and made no attempt to walk. He had a complete physical check-up and nothing was physically wrong.

The physiotherapist tried in many ways to encourage Joe to get the 'feel of his feet'. Joe resisted and screamed when his feet touched the ground. The playleader watched the physiotherapist and was with Joe while he had treatment. They discussed how play might stimulate Joe to make progress in walking. At first Joe began to play more actively lying on a rug on the floor. He liked to grasp the playleader's hands and pull himself up to a sitting position. He did not like being put in a 'baby-walker' and curled his feet up—but he gradually accepted this for ten minutes at a time.

For several weeks he progressed in active play with bricks, balls, rattles, wooden spoons, etc., but he still disliked using his feet. In the fine weather Joe was taken on to the grass. He enjoyed this and began to press on his feet when held in an upright position. The toys he liked were put on a low chair and when he was held up he actually put his feet on the ground and became interested in playing with bricks. Each day a little progress was made. Sometimes he 'stood' with support on a rug, the grass, a cushion and, eventually, the floor.

The playleader was the only person who could spend unlimited time with him. She helped him use his feet and legs and stimulated his movements when he was involved in play. Three months later he was pushing the baby walker. His mother visited him most days and became friendly with all the staff, the playleader showed her how play activities could help Joe to walk, and how this new ability to move stimulated his development.

Libbie (**2½ years**) was admitted with severely burned face and hands. When the hands were healed but badly marked and disfigured she welcomed opportunities to play with water and clay. The Senior Medical Registrar said that this kind of activity would certainly contribute to recovery.

The Playleader and the Speech Therapist

Playleaders have also co-operated with speech therapists.

Paul (**4 years, 10 months**) had haemophilia and a speech defect. Although very intelligent he had difficulty in pronouncing several 'p'—'pl'—'l' sounds and was frustrated by this. He had speech therapy and the therapist invited the playleader to the treatment room so that Paul could be encouraged to talk during his play using words with these sounds. This presented no difficulties as he loved stories and songs and the playleader was able to incorporate some of the speech exercises into Paul's play. This was such a natural extension of treatment that Paul was completely unaware of the practice he was being given.

The Playleader and the Medical Social Worker

There would seem to be scope for co-operation between playleaders and medical social workers although this has not been developed very much in the hospitals that employ both types of personnel. It can be helpful to parents with problems if they are put in touch with medical social workers by the playleader as in the example of Sonia given in Chapter 3, p. 120.

On one occasion a playleader was asked to visit the home of two sisters (4 and 6 years old) in the ward to advise on how play could be organized in confined space. The playleader recommended a play area under the large kitchen table and arranged regular visits for the children to the local library where there was an excellent range of books and a weekly 'story-time' session. The mother welcomed these suggestions.

Another mother became dependent on the playleader's advice for her subnormal son and when there was a question of transferring him to another hospital the medical social worker asked the playleader to accompany her and the mother to make preliminary arrangements.

The Playleader and Auxiliary Staff, Ward Cleaners, etc.

It is very important for the playleader to have a good relationship with the rest of the ward workers, who have not yet been discussed. Because domestic staff are in and out of the ward all day, serving meals, working in the ward kitchens, cleaning floors, etc., they see quite a lot of the children and their visitors. One example of how a foreign ward domestic helped a small compatriot is described on page 50. Ward staff are often very friendly towards the children and are easily accepted by them as they perform everyday tasks the children are used to seeing their mothers do at home.

Messy play involving sand, water, paint, bits of paper, etc., on the ward floor can make for strain in ward relationships unless the playleaders clean up as scrupulously as possible and unless Sister upholds them in all they do and does not show disapproval in front of ward domestics.

It is hard on cleaners to see their highly polished floors

and tables messed up and they are perhaps the most difficult, as well as the most important people, to convince about the value of play—and especially messy play—for sick children. Some of them are naturally child orientated and the playleader's staunchest allies.

Some hospitals have begun to appoint ward house-keepers and ward clerks to relieve nurses of purely domestic and clerical duties. In the future playleaders may find many opportunities for co-operation with these people whose continuous presence in the same ward should be helpful to the children.

The Playleader and Volunteers

In some children's wards a professional playleader will be assisted by volunteers; in others the playleader may be a voluntary helper herself assisted by a rota of volunteers. Such volunteers may include mothers, members of the W.R.V.S. or Red Cross, pre-nursing students, nursing cadets, student teachers, Scouts, Girl Guides, older school-children. In the United States there is a longstanding tradition of using volunteers extensively in hospitals. This practice is becoming increasingly widespread in this country. In the last few years hospitals have begun to appoint full-time Organizers of Volunteers.[1]

One of the disadvantages of having volunteers on a children's ward is the number of 'new' faces the children may see; this may be very confusing to children already disturbed by admission to hospital. James Robertson says that the provision of volunteers 'may seriously delay recognition of the hospital's responsibility to provide security and love through the mother and/or permanent staff.'[2]

---

[1] *Organizers of Voluntary Services in Hospitals.* By Jan Rocha. King Edward's Hospital Fund for London, 1968.

[2] *Young Children in Hospital.* By James Robertson. Tavistock Publications, 1970.

Volunteers can be very useful in organizing and tidying toy cupboards and in acting as assistants to professional playleaders by preparing paints, clay and other materials before a play session and in tidying and returning all play equipment to storage areas when a session ends. If volunteers are to do more than this with the children they must be given some general instruction about organizing play by the playleader, and this can be supplemented by the use of an information leaflet such as *Working as a Volunteer in a Save the Children Fund Playgroup*[1] which contains much useful advice. It has to be emphasized that volunteers working with children must be regular in attendance as continuity of approach to the children is vital. Each child's current interests can be entered on a card index so that the volunteer can carry on in the playleader's absence. It is essential to impress on volunteers the importance of winning and retaining the goodwill of all nursing staff and of the domestic cleaners—as the SCF leaflet says: 'The sweeping of scattered sand and mopping up of spilt water or paint are often necessary!'

In practice one sometimes finds a particular volunteer working many hours a week in a children's ward and very much part of the place, trusted by the nursing staff and regarded by the children as a kind of foster-mother—or grandmother—according to age.

Male volunteers are much appreciated, particularly by older children. They can help with carpentry projects and in mending the children's equipment and furniture. At Moorfields Hospital they have a plumber among their volunteers and at Great Ormond Street several members of the police force take children on outside expeditions, and a mounted policeman amuses the children by riding slowly round the outside of the hospital buildings.

Young people are often keen to work in hospitals—

---

[1] Save the Children Fund, 29 Queen Anne's Gate, S.W.1

especially with children. This can be a useful experience and may help them to embark eventually on a hospital profession. With careful organization playleaders should be able to make good use of this fund of energy and goodwill.

6

Some Hospital Play Schemes Overseas

Organized play facilities for children in hospital are now being provided in many parts of the world. The few schemes described here have been selected because they are personally known to the authors and incorporate some interesting individual features. The reports are quoted from original sources directly associated with the schemes themselves.

AMERICA

A hospital's recognition of the value of play for sick children varies as widely in the United States hospitals as it does in the United Kingdom. The move to think through and to humanize the treatment of children in United States hospitals has come from within the hospital professions and has not focused exclusively on the special needs of one particular age group. There is no lay movement of parents in America similar to the National Association for the Welfare of Children in Hospital in this country. All hospitalized children from birth to teenage are the concern of the 'American Association for Child Care in the Hospital' formed in 1967. Its several hundred members include paediatricians, paedriatric surgeons, nurses, social workers and large numbers of hospital child care workers—of whom there is no exact English equivalent. They work in hospitals throughout the United States and Canada, focusing on the psychological and social aspects of hospital care of children and their families. Parents may become associate members. A majority of the professional members are involved in running 'Child Life

Programs' in children's wards. The setting up of such a 'program' in a hospital usually involves even more than the establishment of a playgroup in a U.K. hospital. Child care workers who organize the 'program' will be trained in child development, or education, or both, and will provide interesting creative play for the younger children, teaching for the school-age child, exciting projects for teenage patients and in general work for the well-being of all young patients. Unrestricted visiting, rooming-in for mothers, preparation for treatment and surgery, care of the resident mother, parent counselling, will all be aspects of the family-based paediatric care envisaged by a 'Child Life Program'.[1]

The organizers of the Child Life programs described in more detail below have all been concerned with setting up the American Association for Child Care in the Hospital.

A. *Children's Medical and Surgical Centre, Johns Hopkins Hospital, Baltimore*

This is one of the world's leading children's hospitals. The discussions of a remarkable multi-disciplinary team of doctors, nurses and child development specialists[2] led to the development of a child life program for all wards including intensive care unit, surgical, infants and toddlers, teenage, long-term and paediatric clinical research unit, also in out-patients and in the hospital welfare clinic run for children of poor inner-city families. The Play-Education program has a Director, Assistant Director and 20 employees.

All mothers of two- to six-year-olds are asked to room

---

[1] 'American Association for Child Care in Hospital' by A. Hales-Tooke. *Maternal and Child Care*. Vol. IV, No. 33. January 1968.

[2] *The Hospitalized Child and his Family.* Edited by J. A. Haller, M.D., Oxford University Press, 1968.

in if possible and mothers of older children, if this is the first hospitalization. Mothers are looked after by a Living-in Co-ordinator who deals with any problems and with staff-parent relationships. One hundred and eighty mothers can room in at once. In April 1969, 104 mothers lived in. Home helps can go into houses to relieve mothers so that they can room in.

Mothers are invited to join in the play programme. Playrooms on most floors can be divided with hinged partitions for pre-school play and more formal teaching of school-age children.

Daily Schedule

9.00 a.m.	Child Life Workers discuss the children with the head nurse.
9.30	Workers arrange play/school areas and fetch the children.
	Free play/formal teaching.
11.30	Organized activity.
12.00	Lunch 'family style', children, mothers, child-care workers.
1.00–2.30 p.m.	Rest for all children.
2.30–6.00	Film show, outing, individual attention for bed-fast children.
6.00	Supper.
7.00–9.00	Evening activities with volunteers for older children.

As in most United States hospitals the physical facilities are superb. There are even comfortable waiting areas for parents outside the operating theatres and ample, well-arranged indoor and outdoor play space. Every kind of play and educational aid is available.

B. *Bellevue Hospital Center, New York*

This has had a specially organized Recreation Service for children since 1949. Besides providing for Bellevue's 200 child patients (100 are psychiatric patients) in the last few years the service organizers have enlarged their activities to include such things as a swimming programme for children in the local community.

There is a staff of 25 most of whom work directly with the children; others work indirectly in the office, or with supplies and equipment. Having two Spanish-speaking staff members has helped tremendously.[1] An active corps of volunteers trained and supervised by the staff, work on the wards and in the playrooms all day. An average of 65 volunteers a month gave 7,256 hours last year.[2] Each year for the past 12 years, one of the volunteers has organized a Christmas window-painting project. There is a youth volunteer service programme for senior school children and a student training programme.

An outstanding programme is run with imagination and a readiness to explore new untried areas, e.g. music therapy. The following are a few extracts from the latest available Annual Report:[1]

Infants and Toddlers Ward

'This is an admitting ward for children with illnesses such as pneumonia, congenital heart disease, neurological problems, neglect and battering, age range from newborn infants to three-year-olds.

'The ward is usually filled with 15 to 20 babies and 4 or 5 toddlers. We have a mobile hanging from the ceiling and each crib has a busy box or a colourful or appropriate toy attached for the baby to rattle and explore.

---

[1] *Twenty-First Annual Report, 1969.* Recreation Service for Children, Bellevue Hospital Center, 27 Street and First Avenue, New York, N.Y. 10016.

[2] *Volunteer Manual.* Recreation Service for Children, Bellevue Hospital Center.

'We first started this program by asking a psychologist who had done research work with babies to come and spend an afternoon on our ward and speak at a staff meeting about the importance of working as early as possible with babies.

'The tiny ones are settled in colourful tenders. They enjoy looking at all their surroundings and notice all the people around them. A few are in the playpen and the toddlers are allowed to walk or run about with pull toys. We now have a soft rug for the babies who are just learning to crawl or enjoy relaxing or rolling on the floor.

Orthopaedic Ward

'One of the special interests of the 15 to 20 boys and girls on this ward has been the growing of vegetables, flowers and trees in their balcony garden.

'A dynamic young scoutmaster and a rotating committee of scouts from the community helped our Boy Scouts earn their tenderfoot awards this year.

Adolescent Program

'Since our census of adolescents is higher than ever before, we are developing a daily program to meet their needs. The traditional rest hour between 1 and 2 p.m. is their special time. They assemble in the main playroom and have three craft sessions and two music sessions a week. Sometimes the playroom is converted into a beauty parlour and the girls have manicures and hair-dos.'

There are special play programs in the Rubella Nursery for multi-handicapped children which also has a special education and training program for student nurses, doctors, occupational therapists, etc., which is orientated to both the hospital and the community. There are several other nurseries for mentally handicapped and disturbed pre-school children including one in which the children go home at weekends. Here many efforts are made to involve the parents and to link the child's home and hospital life.

C. *Boston Floating Hospital*

This hospital is now the 100-bed paediatric unit of the New England Medical Center Hospitals. It started in 1893 on a boat anchored in Boston harbour as a refuge for mothers and their sick children suffering especially from the humid summers' infectious diseases.

A play program for all the children has been developed since 1947 as part of the Paediatric Psychiatric service in the hospital. It is run by four full-time nursery school teachers who 'are in constant working contact with the psychiatrists concerning the special problems presented by individual children'. They work from 8.30 a.m. to 5 p.m. Each is assigned to certain children in small groups, but all work in the one big room—giving each other mutual support especially with the terminal patients.

An English observer described the playroom atmosphere as very relaxed and permissive. 'Lots of mothering was being done—playladies, students and volunteers were assigned to hold and cuddle children up to four years old including one from a deprived inner city family who had been kept shut up in the dark and had eye trouble. They also changed nappies and helped with feeding. There was a very democratic relationship with the doctors, one boy remarking, "Here comes that dumb dumb doctor!" It is one of the very few United States hospitals where children wear dayclothes.

'The teachers are sensitive women, trained and experienced with children. They wear colourful smocks, offer toys and good food and what is frequently more important they offer a lap for the forlorn little ones to sit in, praise when praise is due, and a firm and kindly "don't" when the child is testing to the limits.'[1]

On the top floor there is a Family Participation Unit where parents can room in. (There are reduced charges for the children and none for the parents because they are involved in nursing care.) There are weekly conferences for parents with the staff, so that parents can talk about any anxieties stemming from their child's condition.

AUSTRALIA

The following extracts are from a report provided by the Australian Pre-School Association:[2]

A. *Margaret Reid Hospital, St. Ives, New South Wales*

'Most of the nursery school children in the hospital are at stages of immobilization on bed frames or walking. Rehabilitation and so play experiences, though not denied or restricted because of a disability, have to be made adaptable in most cases.

'For those capable of physical activity there is outdoor equipment, consisting of swings, slides, swimming pool, climbing bars, etc.: these are meant to be all-purpose and are not specially designed to meet the needs of the pre-school child.

'One of the most important and valuable pieces of equipment is a miniature cottage consisting of dining-room, lounge, kitchen and bathroom which we have

---

[1] 'A Play Program for Hospitalized Children: The Role of the Playroom Teacher.' By Y. B. Tisza and K. Angoft, *Pediatrics*, November 1961.

[2] Australian Pre-School Association, Acton Offices, Canberra City, A.C.T. 2601, Australia.

found essential for training these children who have been hospitalized for a number of years away from a home environment of which they have had little experience.

'Those confined to bed are provided as far as possible with normal "messy" play within the limits of their handicap with materials such as sand, water, play dough, and bricks. To substitute for the normal large physical movements involved in such play an endeavour is made to extend its scope by the use of as many varied implements as can be thought of which can be satisfactorily handled in small tubs of water or trays of sand, etc., at a bedside.

'Hammer toys, peg boards, insets, etc., are, with the exception of those children with a manual handicap, used in the normal manner. One of the most difficult problems of the immobilized child is the development of group sense and the provision for creative play within the groups. In this regard it would seem that the play situations must be essentially teacher-centred to provide the child-to-child link which is physically impossible otherwise.

'This involves, in such activities as playing with dolls, the delegation by the teacher of specific play situations to the children and explanation of the general type of play required. For many children who have come from home at the age of two to three and have been hospitalized for 12 to 18 months there is little understanding of the relevance of washing up, hanging clothes, going shopping, etc., and generally the teacher has to direct the children to the background and to the language association with such background.

'Each activity is supplemented with as much material from books and visual aids as can be found to assist the child to find the fullest possible meaning in his play.

'The teacher's role in the initial stage is thus a rather

directive one as suggested, in stimulating and in interpreting for other members of the group so that they may appreciate each other's play.

'Similarly in painting activities the teacher must act as link within the group transferring the knowledge gained by experiment with material and tools from one member of the group to the other.

'House play and dramatic play associated with it are very popular but again the restriction of experience calls for a great deal of teacher direction in early stages. For those children in bed desiring to "dress up" the emphasis is of necessity on as wide a variety as possible of hats, head scarves, jewellery, make-up, and all the accessories which can be devised for the situations, e.g. handbags, baskets, artificial flowers, purses, brief cases, tool boxes, yachting caps, beach bags, umbrellas, etc. Even if the handicap does not permit the full dressing of the child it has been found that the laying of a garment over the child, e.g. boiler suit, swimming costume, has provided a good deal of satisfaction.'

B. *The Royal Children's Hospital, Parkville, Victoria*

This hospital provides play opportunities for children at several levels.

'A child-minding centre staffed by voluntary aides cares for siblings of patients attending the hospital. A well-equipped playroom and outdoor play-space is provided.

'A Cerebral Palsy Unit, staffed by trained kindergarteners, and a play leader, operates for pre-school children, who are brought in by Red Cross drivers. These children attend in small groups and spaced attendance is necessary.

'The Occupational Therapy Department caters for all children in hospital. There are two well-equipped rooms where children who are mobile can come to from the wards. One is staffed by a trained kinder-gartener, and caters for pre-school children. The other is used by occupational therapists and children attend in different age groups.

'Each ward is staffed by an occupational therapist who provides suitable occupation for all children who are confined to bed.

'Each ward also has a playroom which may be used by occupational therapists, nurses, voluntary helpers and parents. Two wards have a balcony which may be used by children for outdoor play.

'Parents are encouraged to come regularly to play with their children and are welcome any time except during the afternoon rest period.

'It is often a joy to see a father drop in on his way home from work to play with his child.

'The Department of Psychiatry has two play therapists who cater for disturbed children, both In-patients and Out-patients. These children attend by appointment. A trained Psychiatric Sister and play therapist have a playroom for long-term cases where they can be free to play without disturbing the ward.

'Each room occupied by a psychiatrist or psychol-ogist is equipped with play material and in the use of this, disturbed children are helped to solve their problems.

'The orthopaedic section at Mount Eliza has a trained kindergartener in charge, and a kindergarten room especially equipped for use by physically handicapped children.

'Occupational Therapists work with children in the wards.'

C. *Princess Margaret Hospital for Children, Perth, Western Australia*

'The Play (or diversionary) Therapy Unit is under the control of the Occupational Therapist-in-Charge, and the girls employed as play therapists work individually in the various wards or as a group when a number of ambulants can be congregated in the playroom.

'Each ward is at ground level and has an adjacent grassed area containing swings and/or slides. On suitable days many beds are wheeled from the ward to the nearby lawns.

'Each ward building (pavilion type) has a rocking horse and a substantial number of books and toys. Children in bed are provided with sets of toys from the Occupational Therapy Department, and these are mainly constructional toys, ranging from simple "pile ups" to Meccano sets; simple train sets, jigsaw puzzles, mosaic sets and cutting out facilities.

'The playroom normally caters for pre-school ambulants from all wards, and during school holidays it also makes provision for the younger school children.'

CANADA

A. *Montreal Children's Hospital*

Mrs. Carolyn L. Keleny, Director of the Play Department at Montreal Children's Hospital, writes:[1]

'Montreal is a very special hospital of 350 beds which serves children of many cultural and linguistic backgrounds, French, English and Eskimo included. It has

---

[1] *Newsletter of the American Association for Child Care in Hospitals*, No. 6, March 1970. P.O. Box 347, Cleveland, Ohio, 44127, U.S.A.

a wide reputation for its advanced medical treatment and relaxed, warm atmosphere, with a staff that is continually seeking new ways to improve the quality of care.

Play Department

'Similar to many programs for hospitalized children, our aims are to foster normal development in a broad sense, and to help children cope as effectively as possible with the hospital experience. The core of the program is direct work with the children (either in groups or individually) by qualified staff through appropriate activities and with a helping relationship. The staff directs volunteer-assistants and helps to guide the one-week learning experience for student nurses.

Current Endeavours

'Recently we have opened a service on our Isolation Unit and are exploring ways to increase supportive human contact and sensory stimulation; through changes in decor and installation of inter-room telephones, for example. We are concerned about programming for infants, particularly in the absence of the parents' participation, and are re-establishing a program temporarily discontinued for financial reasons. Spurred on by a very successful and illuminating experimental program in the Out-patients Department this summer, we are working toward the establishment of a full-time program in this area. Serving the family as a unit, this program would include child care education as a goal.

Play-nursing Collaboration

'Staff and nurses enjoy getting to know each other as persons as well as representatives of disciplines when the nurses join us for one week. A program is set up with their particular needs and interests in mind and our door is always open. All nursing instructors experience this as part of their orientation. Last year all the staff of the Neurosurgery Unit singly rotated through. At present the Recovery Room and Intensive Care nurses are launched in a special experience. Thus we contribute to and complement an already active nursing in-service education program.

'The nursing staff, likewise, is always more than willing to share learning experiences with our staff. We believe that this kind of cordial and meaningful collaboration is very much felt at the level of patient care. (The department, although separate administratively from the Nursing Department, has had a nurse as Director for several years, perhaps partially accounting for the congenial relationship.)

Other Activities

'Daily cuddling-socializing-stimulating visits may be requested for a long-term premature baby when the nursing staff is too busy.

'The receiving area of the Operating Room is stocked with appropriate toys. If they are not remembered, our department is reminded.

'Arrangements may be made to send photographs to a child's family which is far from Montreal.'

B. *Hospital Sainte Justine, Montreal*

This French hospital for children with 800 beds has 25 per cent of its patients less than two years old and 43 per cent less than five years old. Many children come from hundreds of miles to the hospital so may have no visitors throughout their stay. Here the Director of Volunteer Service, with a training in hospital administration and with six children of her own, has built up over the years a very extensive network of volunteers throughout the hospital. This has led to the establishment of a special Play Department called *Milieu Thérapeutique* with professional specialized play staff. Visiting hours are unrestricted and there is some accommodation for mothers to room in. As well as play and teaching on the wards there is a Play Centre on the eighth floor where children do modelling, drawing, oil painting, decorating, pasting and making collections of things. Here they can also listen to records, interpret stories with the aid of puppets and stage plays.

In assessing the use of volunteers in a children's hospital, the Director says:[1]

'Volunteers can be used for the day programs. If the program has been well planned and the job analysis done carefully they can be of great help in a child-activity program. A job description for the volunteers will be made and written instructions given to them. A close relationship should exist between the Director of Nursing, the Director of the Child Activity Program and the Director of Volunteers, as the volunteer is often asked to feed the children and play with them. At St. Justine's our college and university students are marvellous with children and adolescents. The staff and patients and their families are delighted with our young men students who are gay, willing and enthusiastic. They are a godsend to our boys—so glad to discuss hockey, exchange opinions of the players, make stamp collections and play games.

'With our volunteers, we can emphasize the person-to-patient relationship in well-directed companionship. Our students invited Rogation Vachon, the Canadians' goalie, to our department as a surprise volunteer; they obtained free tickets for a hockey game for a boy

---

[1] 'What Volunteers have to offer a Children's Hospital' by Fernande L. Robitaille, *Canadian Hospital*, December 1970.

suffering from leukaemia; they also obtained auto-graphed photos and hockey sticks from the players of many American teams. Students make friends with children convalescing after treatment in hospitals and even visit them in their homes. Many of our girls have worked as counsellors at summer camps or in park recreation programs, and we can hear them singing and playing games, laughing with the children.

'The evening program at St. Justine's involves many office girls who are reliable and in need of basic human relations after a hard day of routine work. An evening co-ordinator is then needed.

'On Sunday afternoons, the younger volunteers (under 17) take charge of the patients' younger brothers and sisters who are unable to visit. At times we have as many as 30 or 40 children in the lobby waiting for their parents. In addition to manning the toy cart and library cart, volunteers also meet new patients at the admitting desk with a friendly smile and warm personal greeting and advise parents to visit as often and for as long as possible.

'We also have an arts and crafts program where volunteers assist the professional educator in stimulating the children's interest in these areas. They also help the other professional educator in taking children to and from the gym and swimming programs. The "out door clinics" can also benefit greatly from the use of volunteers.'

HOLLAND

Academisch Ziekenhuis, Leiden

In 1953 a teacher was appointed to the paediatric unit of this University Hospital, and in 1958 a playroom was built. There are now (1971) several trained play therapists and about eight student play therapists working as a play staff team alongside the hospital staff, with whom they have weekly discussion meetings. This work is psychoanalytically orientated under the guidance of Professor Veeneklaas.

Each child has a typed programme for the day and treatments are given early and not during the times put down for play. Playroom space and offices for the play staff are spacious and the equipment is excellent. Besides guinea pigs in the playroom the children look after goats that are kept in the playroom garden.

Children are flown into Leiden for treatment from other countries in the care of an air hostess. Each child is met at the airport by a play therapist who looks after him throughout his hospital stay.

'The play therapists receive a special training which includes nursing, teaching and child development studies. These girls are responsible for play in the wards and when a child is to undergo a serious operation, one of the play therapists, already well known to the child, is allocated to the patient with whom she not only plays, but eats and sleeps for at least 24 hours before the operation. She accompanies the child to the operating theatre and is again at the bedside when the child regains consciousness and will remain in this close companionship until the doctor feels the child is sufficiently well to manage without it. The doctor-professor in charge of this unit is so convinced of the value of this service that he will no longer operate without the help of the play therapist. Although he encourages visits from parents he feels the emotional strain for them to go through such an ordeal with their own children would be too great and he prefers to use his own staff, who know the procedures and how they may deviate.'[1]

---

[1] 'Imaginative Play for Children in Hospital' by S. Harvey. *Maternal and Child Care*, Vol. 1, No. 3, July 1965.

Over the past few years two play therapists from Leiden have worked for periods of time in a Save the Children Fund playgroup at Fulham Hospital at the suggestion of Dr. Hugh Jolly and SCF play staff have visited Leiden. The English playleaders have been impressed by the detailed care with which the Dutch play therapists prepare and handle a child during treatment. For instance, to prepare a five-year-old for a lumbar puncture after a discussion about pricks and the administration of a sedative the therapist tells the story of a kitten who loves to sleep curled up tightly in a ball. The story is elaborated in a quiet soothing voice and the therapist suggests he could be like the kitten and curl into a ball. This is the necessary position for a lumbar puncture. Once asleep if the child is small enough the therapist then carries him to the treatment room where the treatment is given as he lies on her lap.

Important points to bear in mind about Leiden are:
(1) Parents have a very small part to play in their child's hospital stay.
(2) The nurses also have a different role compared with nurses in the U.K.
(3) The high proportion of play therapists to patients, sometimes 1:3.
(4) The play therapists are trained on the ward having previously done a four-year mothercraft training starting at 16 years of age.

SWEDEN

Extracts from a Report by Mrs. Ivonny Lindquist, head play therapist, Umea Hospital:[1]

---

[1] Mrs. Lindquist is the author of the book *Terapi Genom Lek* (Therapy through play) available in Sweden (1970).

'In 1909 a Finnish kindergarten teacher, Barbi Luther, started play and occupational activity in hospital in *Helsinki*, Finland. The idea spread from there to Sweden and play activity was started for children in 1912 in The Crown Princess Louisa's Nursing Home for Sick Children in *Stockholm*. Up to 1930 kindergarten teachers[1] and voluntary workers organized play activities for children in sanatoria and long-term hospitals without salaries or grants. In 1930 the first paid kindergarten teacher was appointed and play therapy organized by nursery school teachers is now found in a number of Swedish hospitals and clinics. It has always been felt in Sweden that play therapy for sick and handicapped children should be organized by trained teachers. There has been resistance to the idea that financial backing is needed if their work is to be done properly. Teachers Training Colleges in *Stockholm* and *Malmo* run a one-year special course for nursery school teachers wanting to work with children in hospital.

'Most Swedish children get play therapy if they are in children's wards but not if they are in adult wards. *Umea University Hospital* is exceptional in having play for children in both types of ward. A hundred children come daily in beds, wheel chairs, or by walking, to a large play therapy department run by three nursery school teachers. Between 8 to 9.30 a.m. the day's activities are prepared by teachers, assistants and student teachers. A nursery school teacher takes a trolley with play material to the children not able to come to the department. The other two teachers work with individual children, practising movement with a handicapped child, doing motor tests, making observations. Between 9.30 and 11 a.m. children come from the wards

---

[1] Kindergarten teachers have a two-year training course in Sweden which is an amalgamation of the National Nursery Examination Board and primary teacher's course in the U.K.

and do what they feel like doing. They have a choice of playroom, a reading and rest room, a play kitchen, a workshop and a teenage room. At 11 a.m. lunch is served in the wards and the children rest until 1 p.m. Thereafter strings of children come to the play therapy department, often with their parents, until 4 p.m.

'It is interesting to see how well they get on together—handicapped and normal children covering a 3 to 15 years age group. The teachers only direct the activities of these children who need to practise certain functions —not only motor functions, but also intellectual, emotional and social aspects of daily life.

'The teachers observe, inspire and stimulate the children through encouragement and personal involvement so that the children feel secure and ready to play despite illness and possible handicap. At team conferences the teachers participate fully with the doctors, physiotherapists, nurses and social workers and take part in planning the continued training of the handicapped children both in the hospital and later at home. The teachers also run an extensive advisory service for parents on suitable play material and its uses.

'We have also equipped 10 wards with toys which we look after. From these toy stores staff and parents can get play material for the children so that no child need be without playthings. We have also put toys in 30 waiting rooms as we feel it is very important that children arriving at the hospital should find it friendly from the start. Parents have often told us that on returning home from hospital children remember not "the prick in the finger" but the toy car and doll's pram. This makes it easier when the child has to re-visit the clinic.

'We feel we have a very important task in the hospital to inform and instruct other staff on how to handle children. Many of the staff do not know about the educational material we are using, nor do they understand the need to give children play material which is suitable for their age and level of development. Those of us trained to interpret children's ways of communicating must speak up for them and fight for their rights when they are away from home in a frightening situation and in a lowered general condition and when they need a maximum amount of encouragement, love and security.'

It seems from this report that a greater emphasis on the children's psychological needs may be made in the future in Sweden's play therapy programmes in hospitals, which previously seemed exclusively pre-occupied with providing children with interesting occupations.

Appendix 1

Working as a Volunteer in a Save the Children Fund Playgroup

A playgroup is designed for children to play actively and creatively. While they are playing they develop healthy bodies and lively minds. They have opportunities for meeting and mixing with children of their own age under the guidance of an understanding adult. Speech is very important; children will welcome people who are ready to talk to them and to listen to what they have to say. In this way they will enlarge their vocabularies.

Plenty of natural materials are available such as sand, water, clay and paint as well as a wide variety of occupations both indoors and outside. This experience will later be organized into knowledge.

Children need encouragement and interest in their achievements; they may need help to make progress in their play, but most of all they need to develop their own activities in their own way without interference of older people. It is most important that children express their own feelings and ideas, particularly in creative activities, so that it is unwise to draw for them or to suggest that they copy from books, or to tell them what to draw or make. However poor the results may appear to be, they should be appreciated, and no attempt made by an adult to 'improve' their work. Your own interest in craft or music will often stimulate the children's interest.

A child absorbed in an occupation should not be disturbed. The only precautions that are necessary are that they should not hurt themselves or others nor be destructive of equipment. Children usually only undertake adventures which they can successfully carry through. They are usually the best judges of the risks they can safely manage, so they should not be urged to go beyond what they think they can manage, e.g. to climb higher than they feel confident to go, nor discouraged by unnecessary warnings of 'Be careful!', 'Take care!' They need to be in the care of people who have confidence in their abilities.

On starting work in a playgroup try to discover what each child wants to do rather than pressing him to do what you think he would like to do.

Many of the children come from limited home backgrounds so do not try to talk about things outside their own observation and experience: conversation about things they have not experienced themselves will be meaningless to them. It is only when you can really enter into their world that you can help them to make progress in all their activities. It helps a child to communicate with an adult if she bends or sits so that she is on a level with him when talking or listening to him.

Sometimes it is a temptation to spend a great deal of time with one child who appeals to you, for in any group you belong to everyone, and must share yourself with all the children; they will expect fair recognition from you.

The only exception may be a difficult child who will need your help because he cannot play constructively and may be destructive and break up the play of others. This child needs sympathetic help and support and it is rewarding to watch the progress he makes through your interest in him. Praise his positive achievements; if he is persistently destructive, try to find acceptable outlets for his destructiveness, like building and knocking down building blocks or sand castles, banging nails or a hammer toy, smacking dolls rather than other children.

Always refer to the person in charge for advice on discipline.

Little children need to be looked after in a consistent

way. Watch how the playgroup leader talks to the children and co-operate with her in the management of them. Never make a promise to a child which you cannot keep. It is important for children to build confidence in adults, and a broken promise is a serious offence to a child. Always answer a child's questions honestly; he means seriously whatever he says, and it is important to treat it seriously.

It may often be useful to discuss a particular child with the leader, but it is important to ensure that this is not done in the child's presence.

You should arrive about half an hour before the playgroup opens in order to help in setting out the equipment and preparing the activities before the children arrive. Your help will also be needed in putting away everything at the end of the session. You will be shown the way in which the materials and equipment are stored, everything should be clean, tidy and mended if possible. This is an important part of your job. The sweeping of scattered sand and mopping up of spilt water or paint are often necessary. It is helpful to keep an eye on puzzles and sets of toys so that the pieces are not lost.

The playleader will welcome any new ideas or suggestions for activities which you may have. If you enjoy the children they will enjoy your visit and your help will be appreciated by everyone.

S. HARVEY
M. MONK-JONES

Appendix 2

Taking a Child to another Department

When taking a child to another department remember . . .

The child has no idea where he is going; how long he will be away; if he is to be brought back.

He does not know what is going to be done to him.

He will be afraid his parents do not know where to find him.

It will be a great help to the child if you explain what is happening as fully and as truthfully as possible, reassuring where necessary. If a child is too young for verbal explanation he should be reassured by the presence of his mother. If this cannot be arranged he should be accompanied by someone he knows from his own ward, who will stay with him and bring him back.

If it is expected the child is in for a long wait, provide for his comfort and entertainment whilst waiting. He may need books, toys, orange juice, tissues and possibly a change of nappy.

Don't forget to talk to the child, explain all the new things he sees and make his visit as interesting and enjoyable as possible. You will probably find you enjoy the visit more and that the child is more co-operative.

All these points also apply to a child going to another ward for surgery. However, the child will need even more reassurance about returning and seeing his parents later. Most older children have a deep fear of anaesthetics. The child should never be left alone on a strange ward.

Someone he knows should wait by his bed, playing, talking or just cuddling him until the pre-medication takes effect.

You will probably be allowed to accompany the child to the anaesthetic room; the child will then see a familiar face until he becomes unconscious.

Again, someone he knows should be by the bed when he begins to recover consciousness. This can be a confused and frightening time. Gently remind him where he is, what has happened and tell him he will soon feel better.

EVE LATIMER, SCF hospital playleader

Appendix 3

National Association for the Welfare of Children in Hospital

The formation of Mother Care for Children in Hospital (MCCH) by a small group of mothers in Battersea, London, in 1961 was the direct result of the publication in the *Observer* of a series of articles by James Robertson, and the public presentation of his films.[1] The group investigated hospital policies in their own area and found the recommendations of the Platt Report[2] for unrestricted visiting of children and the provision of accommodation for mothers to room-in were being introduced only very slowly—if at all. Other such groups were soon established and in 1963 a national organization was set up which in 1965 changed its name to the National Association for the Welfare of Children in Hospital (NAWCH), and was registered as a charity.

NAWCH is now a thriving movement with more than 60 groups and counts among its members many consultants and other senior hospital staff members, as well as parents. It has 'excellent standing in the community, and a consistently good national press'.[3] From the outset the Association has seen as its main function the need to persuade hospitals that the new concepts in child care are worth while and that they do work, and to persuade

---

[1] J. Robertson: *A Two Year Old Goes to Hospital* (1952); *Going to Hospital with Mother* (1958). Tavistock Child Development Research Unit.

[2] Ministry of Health: *The Welfare of Children in Hospital*. H.M.S.O, 1959.

[3] J. Robertson: *Young Children in Hospital—with a Postscript 1970*. Tavistock Publications.

parents that they themselves have a major role to play in the care of their sick children.

NAWCH undertakes surveys to determine actual ward practice,[1] and maintains an up-to-date information service for parents about the shifts and changes in paediatric wards throughout the country. It will advise and help parents to get their children into the most suitable wards, and will support those who question the prohibitions of restrictive wards.

NAWCH groups provide a variety of local welfare services. These include crèches for siblings of child patients, car pool services, hospitality and accommodation for mothers visiting hospitals from long distances, the provision of sensible day clothes and suitable toys for children's wards. Fund raising by local NAWCH groups has helped to provide specially built or converted mother and child units, and to pay for playleaders and play facilities.

NAWCH has campaigned for the improvement of facilities for children in out-patients and accident/emergency departments, the provision of more home-care services, the extension of day-operations, the separation of children from adult patients, the provision of playleaders in all children's wards. Above all, the Association stresses the need for the teaching of child development in nurse and medical training programmes to take much greater account of the child's emotional needs. It has helped to initiate research to determine the pattern of nursing care

---

[1] NAWCH survey of Visiting (1969) indicates:

1. Only 57 per cent of hospitals allow unrestricted visiting;
2. 25 per cent do not allow morning visiting;
3. 35 per cent allow visiting on day of operation for ear, nose and throat patients;
4. 10 per cent routinely offer accommodation for mothers of young children.

NAWCH: *Coming into Hospital*—Hospital Admission Leaflet (see page 140). Obtainable from: N.A.W.C.H.

best suited to the needs of the long-stay child and supports those who press for more research into the indication and benefits of tonsillectomy for children.

NAWCH has worked effectively to promote the Platt Report both within the Health Service and the community. Through its own publications, and its wide newspaper and television coverage it aims to achieve an informed public opinion in which the needs of the sick child will be fully recognized.

Finally, the Association has had an international impact. Similar Associations have been formed in Australia, New Zealand, Canada and Eire, while the American Association for Child Care in Hospitals, founded in 1967, has close links with NAWCH.

Mrs A. Hales-Tooke has represented NAWCH for this publication.

Appendix 4

What is OMEP?

The World Organization for Early Childhood Education, known as OMEP from the French title (Organisation Mondiale pour l'Education Préscolaire), was founded in 1948. Its main tasks are to promote greater understanding of children under eight years of age and to share between different countries the experience and knowledge gained through the study of young children during their formative years.

OMEP is an international, non-governmental educational organization and membership is open to any organization and person of any race, creed or nationality.

National Committees are working in thirty-four countries (1971). These include: Australia, Austria, Belgium, Brazil, Canada, Chile, Denmark, Finland, France, W. Germany, Greece, Israel, Ireland (Eire), Italy, Norway, Philippines, South Africa, Spain, Sweden, United Kingdom, United States of America, Uruguay and Yugoslavia.

International Assemblies are held every three years on some aspect of early childhood education.

OMEP has consultative status with UNESCO, UNICEF and the United Nations Commission for Economic and Social Affairs and co-operates with other organizations having related interests.

Mrs Susan Harvey is the Vice Chairman of the UK National Committee.
Authors' royalties from this book will go to OMEP.

Bibliography

GENERAL DEVELOPMENT AND PLAY

Allen, Lady, of Hurtwood, *Planning for Play*. Thames & Hudson, 1968.

B.B.C., *How to form a Playgroup*. B.B.C. Publications, 1970.

Blackie, J., *Inside the Primary School*. H.M.S.O., 1972.

Bowlby, J., *Child Care and the Growth of Love*. Pelican, 1965.

Brearley, M. and Hitchfield, E., *A Teacher's Guide to reading Piaget*. Routledge and Kegan Paul, 1966.

Chesters, G., *The Mothering of Young Children*. Faber and Faber, 1956.

Cunningham, P. J., *Nursery Nursing*. Faber and Faber, 1967.

Erikson, E. H., *Childhood and Society*. Pelican, 1969.

Gardner, D. E. M., *The Education of Young Children*. Methuen, 1956.

Gesell, A., *The First Five Years of Life*. Methuen, 1966.

Gesell, A., *The Child from Five to Ten*. Hamish Hamilton, 1946.

Ginott, H. G., *Between Parent and Child*. Staples Press, 1969.

Hartley, Frank and Goldenson, *Understanding Children's Play*. Routledge and Kegan Paul, 1952.

Hostler, P., *The Child's World*. Penguin, 1965.

H.M.S.O., *Our Young Children*. 1969.

Isaacs, S., *The First Two Years*. Nursery School Association, 1940.

Isaacs, S., *The Nursery Years*. Routledge and Kegan Paul, 1968 (second edition).

Isaacs, S., *The Psychological Aspects of Child Development*. Evans Brothers, 1965.

Isaacs, S., *Intellectual Growth in Young Children*. Routledge and Kegan Paul, 1930, 10th impression 1970.

Isaacs, S., *Social Development in Young Children*. Routledge and Kegan Paul, 1933, 9th impression 1967.

Jameson, K., *Pre-School and Infant Art*. Studio Vista, 1969.

de Lissa, L., *Life in the Nursery School*. Longmans, 1949.

Lowenfeld, M., *Play in Childhood*. Gollancz, 1935.

Marshall, S., *An Experiment in Education*. Cambridge University Press, 1963.

O.M.E.P., *Your Child is Growing*. 1970.

Pickard, P. M., *The Activity of Children*. Longmans, 1965.

Sheridan, M. D., *The Developmental Progress of Infants and Young Children*. H.M.S.O., 1967.

Tavistock Clinic Series, *Your Baby to The Teenager*. Corgi Mini-books. Transworld, 1970.

Tudor-Hart, B., *Growth through Play in the First Two Years*. National Society of Children's Nurseries, 1968.

Wall, W. D. and Freud, A., *The Enrichment of Childhood*. N.S.A., 1960.

Winnicott, D. W., *The Child, the Family and the Outside World*. Penguin, 1971.

Winnicott, D. W., *Playing and Reality*. Tavistock Publications, 1971.

PLAY, EDUCATION, AND SICKNESS

Bergmann, T. and Freud, A., *Children in the Hospital*. International Universities Press, 1965.

Cass, J. E., 'Play and the Young Child.' *Spastic Quarterly*. June, 1963.

Davidson, E. R., 'Play for the Hospitalised Child.' *American Journal of Nursing*, March, 1949.

Finnie, Nancie R., *Handling the Young Cerebral Palsied Child at Home*. Heinemann, 1968.

Freud, A., *The Role of Bodily Illness in the Mental Life of Children*. *Psychoanalytic Study of the Child*, 1952.

Gould, J., *The Prevention of Damaging Stress in Children*. J. & A. Churchill, 1968.

Hales-Tooke, A., 'Play in Hospital.' *Maternal and Child Care*, Vol. VI, 64, 1970.

Haller, J. A., *The Hospitalised Child and his Family*. Oxford University Press, 1968.

Harvey, S., 'Play and Education.' *Maternal and Child Care*, Vol. VI, 59, 1970.

McPherson, C. A., 'Educating Children in Hospital.' *Medical World*, August, 1956.

McPherson, C. A., *The Nursery School in an Orthopaedic Hospital*. New Era, March, 1961.

Ministry of Education, *Education of Patients in Hospital*. Circular 312, Sept., 1961.

Ministry of Health, *The Welfare of Children in Hospital*. (Platt Report.) H.M.S.O., 1959.

Nicoll, K. B., *Understanding Traction*. Macmillan (Journals), 1968.

Noble, E., *Play and the Sick Child*. Faber and Faber, 1967.

Plank, E. N., *Working with Children in Hospitals*. Tavistock Publications, 1964.

Prugh, D. G., Staub, Sands, Kirschbaum and Lenihan, 'A Study of the Emotional Reactions of Children and Families to Hospitalisation.' *American Journal of Orthopsychiatry*, 1953, 23, 70.

BIBLIOGRAPHY

Robertson, J., *Young Children in Hospital*. Tavistock Publications, 1970.
Schaffer, H. R. and Callendar, W. M., 'Psychological Effects of Hospitalisation in Infancy.' *Journal of Paediatrics*, 1959, 24, 528.
Stacey, M., Dearden, Roisin and Pill, *Hospitals, Children and their Families*. Routledge and Kegan Paul, 1970.
Spock, B., *Caring for Your Disabled Child*. Macmillan, 1965.
Wolff, S., *Children under Stress*. Allen Lane, Penguin Press, 1969

CHILDREN'S PLAY ACTIVITIES

Boston Children's Medical Center, *What to do when 'there's nothing to do'*. Hutchinson, 1969.
Galt, J. & Co., *Toys and Ideas for Children when Ill*.
Hegler, S., *Choosing Toys for Children*. Tavistock Publications, 1963.
Hutchings, M., *Dolls and How to make Them*. Mills & Boon, 1970 (fourth edition).
Kay, G. and C., *Games and Play for the Sick Child*. Corgi Mini-books, Transworld, 1972.
Matterson, E. M., *Play with a Purpose for Under-Sevens*. Penguin, 1972.
May, E., *Suggestions for Play Activities for Young Children*. S.C.F., 1968.
Septima, *Something to do*. Penguin, 1966.
Tudor-Hart, B., *Play and Toys in Nursery Years*. Country Life, 1938.

Advice about books suitable for every age is available to members of the National Book League, 7 Albemarle Street, London, W.1.

SONG BOOKS

The Puffin Song Book. Compiled by Leslie Woodgate. Puffin Books, 1972.
The Oxford Nursery Song Book. Compiled by Percy Buck. O.U.P., 1961.
The Faber Book of Nursery Songs. Faber and Faber, 1968.

Index

INDEX

sharing, 40, 44, 45
Sheridan, Dr. Mary, 30
Sister, *see* nursing staff
social deprivation, 41, 93, 100, 104 ff.
social play, *see* group play
social worker, 120, 159 ff., 164
South Africa, 192
Spain, 192
'special toy', 36
specialist, play, 143
speech, 31, 34, 38, 45, 47, 50, 53, 94, 95, 98, 109
  therapist, 159
staff nurse, *see* nursing staff
stages of play, 29 ff.
standing, 36, 37, 40
storage of toys and equipment, 131
stories, 40, 41, 45, 48, 53, 133
sucking, 30
supervision of play staff, 146
Sweden, 180–3, 192
symbolic play, 42

talking, 31, 34, 38, 40, 45, 47, 50, 53, 178 ff.
'talking' books, 117
teacher, 146–7
  in hospital, 132, 153–7, 169, 171, 181 ff.

terminal cases, 119 ff., 169
therapist, play, 178 ff.
  speech, 159
toy, hanging, 32
  organization, 128
  special, 36
  storage and maintenance, 131
training, nursing staff, 145, 153, 175
  play staff, 145, 179 ff.
treatment, preparation for, 118 ff.
  support during, 143 ff.

Umea Hospital, Sweden, 180–3
unattractive child, 112 ff.
United Nations, 192
Uruguay, 192

Vaughan, Dr. G. F., 118, 123
Veeneklaas, Professor Dr., 179
visiting, 127, 137, 139 ff.
volunteers, 127, 161 ff., 167, 172, 175, 176–7, 181
  in SCF playgroup, 184 ff.

walking, 37, 38, 44, 46
water play, 40, 43, 49, 54, 57, 61, 95, 111, 159, 162, 171

Yugoslavia, 192